Foreword

This standard has been prepared under the direction of Technical Committee B/504 and is intended for the use of engineers, architects, surveyors, contractors, plumbers and inspection authorities and should also be of general interest. Centralized hot water supply for buildings other than individual dwellings is still covered by CP 342 : Part 2 which should be used in conjunction with this standard. This new edition introduces technical amendments reflecting changes in health and safety requirements but does not constitute a full revision of BS 6700 : 1987 , which is superseded and withdrawn. Further amendments or a full revision of this standard will depend on the progress of prEN 806 and its anticipated publication as a dual standard.

This standard has been written in the form of a practice specification in accordance with PD 6501 : Part 1. In order to comply with this specification, the user has to comply with all of its requirements. It is permissible to depart from recommendations provided there is good reason for doing so.

The design of large scale underground reticulations are not included. Whilst certain aspects of underground systems and the larger storage facilities are dealt with in this standard, it will also be necessary for reference to be made to the procedures of the water supply industry when designing large installations of this nature.

This standard interfaces and overlaps with standards dealing with space heating by hot water. In this respect it has been assumed that this standard should deal with the transmission of both hot and cold water for whatever purpose. The transmission of heat by whatever medium (including water) should clearly be the province of other standards. However, where hot water is the heat transfer medium, the pipework carrying the hot water to the heating apparatus will be of common interest.

The control of the safety of unvented domestic hot water storage systems is included in Building Regulations (see **A.1**).

The normative references listed are predominantly British Standards. As European Standards are published they will replace the relevant British Standards and be the subject of amendment to this publication.

Compliance with a British Standard does not of itself confer immunity from legal obligations.

Summary of pages

This document comprises a front cover, an inside front cover, pages i to iv, pages 1 to 90, an inside back cover and a back cover.

© BSI 1997

iv   *blank*

Section 1. General

1.1 Scope

This standard specifies requirements for and gives recommendations on the design, installation, alteration, testing and maintenance of services supplying water for domestic use within buildings and their curtilages. It covers the system of pipes, fittings and connected appliances installed to supply any building, whether domestic or not, with water for drinking, culinary, domestic laundry, ablutionary, cleaning and sanitary purposes.

This standard deals only with low temperature systems; it does not cover systems that are designed to operate with steam or high temperature hot water (see **1.5.1**).

This standard does not cover domestic central heating systems.

Although many of its recommendations will be applicable, this standard does not cover fire fighting services nor water supply for industrial or other specialist purposes other than to indicate precautions that should be taken when these are used in association with other water services. The point at which a domestic activity becomes an industrial process, e.g. in food preparation, has not been defined and the applicability of this standard will need to be considered in each case.

1.2 References

1.2.1 Normative references

This standard incorporates, by dated or undated reference, provisions from other publications. These normative references are made at the appropriate places in the text and the cited publications are listed on page 85. For dated references, only the edition cited applies; any subsequent amendments to or revisions of the cited publication apply to this standard only when incorporated in the reference by amendment or revision. For undated references, the latest edition of the cited publication applies, together with any amendments.

1.2.2 Informative references

This standard refers to other publications that provide information or guidance. Editions of these publications current at the time of issue of this standard are listed on page 88, but reference should be made to the latest editions.

1.2.3 Statutory references

Statutory references are listed in annex A.

1.3 Definitions

For the purposes of this British Standard the definitions given in BS 6100 : Sections 2.7 and 3.3 apply, together with the following.

1.3.1 backflow

A flow of water in the opposite direction to that intended. It includes back-siphonage, which is backflow caused by siphonage.

1.3.2 building

Any structure (including a floating structure) whether of a permanent character or not, and whether movable or immovable, connected to the water supplier's mains.

1.3.3 cavity wall

Any wall whether structural or partition that is formed by two upright parts of similar or dissimilar building materials suitably tied together with a gap formed between them which may be (but need not be) filled with insulating material.

1.3.4 chase

A recess that is cut into an existing structure.

1.3.5 cover

A panel or sheet of rigid material fixed over a chase, duct or access point, of sufficient strength to withstand surface loadings appropriate to its position.

NOTE. Except where providing access to joints or changes of direction (i.e. at an inspection access point) a cover may be plastered or screeded over.

1.3.6 duct

An enclosure designed to accommodate water pipes and fittings and other services, if required, and constructed so that access to the interior can be obtained either throughout its length or at specified points by removal of a cover or covers.

1.3.7 dwelling

Premises, buildings or part of a building providing accommodation, including a terraced house, a semi-detached house, a detached house, a flat in a block of flats, a unit in a block of maisonettes, a bungalow, a flat within any non-domestic premises, a maisonette in a block of flats, or any other habitable building and any caravan, vessel, boat or houseboat connected to the water supplier's mains.

1.3.8 inspection access point

A position of access to a duct or chase whereby the pipe or pipes therein can be inspected by removing a cover which is fixed by removable fastenings but does not necessitate the removal of surface plaster, screed or continuous surface decoration.

1.3.9 removable fastenings

Fastenings that can be removed readily and replaced without causing damage including turn buckles, clips, magnetic or touch latches, coin operated screws and conventional screws, but do not include nails, pins or adhesives.

1.3.10 sleeve

An enclosure of tubular or other section of suitable material designed to provide a space through an obstruction to accommodate a single water pipe and to which access to the interior can be obtained only from either end of such sleeve.

1.3.11 tap size designations

Numbers directly related to the nominal size of the thread on the inlet of the tap, which in turn is unchanged from the nominal size in inches before metrication, e.g. $\frac{1}{2}$ nominal size tap means a tap with an inlet having a G $\frac{1}{2}$ thread.

1.3.12 walkway or crawlway

An enclosure similar to a duct, but of such size as to provide access to the interior by persons through doors or manholes and which will accommodate water pipes and fittings and other services if required.

1.4 Materials

1.4.1 Choice of material

Pipes, fittings and jointing materials acceptable for water byelaw purposes are listed in the *Water fittings and materials directory* [1] and shall be used within the limits stated in the relevant British Standards and manufacturer's recommendations.

Every pipe, pipe joint and connected fitting shall be capable of withstanding, without damage or deterioration, at the maximum working pressure, sustained temperatures of 40 °C for cold water installations and 95 °C, with occasional short-term excursions in excess of 100 °C to allow for malfunctions, for heated water installations. Discharge pipes connected to temperature or expansion relief valves in unvented hot water systems shall be capable of withstanding any continuous hot water or steam discharge at temperatures up to 125 °C.

If pipes, pipe joints or connected fittings are of dissimilar metals, measures shall be taken to reduce corrosion.

COMMENTARY AND RECOMMENDATIONS ON 1.4.1

Attention is drawn to the building regulations (see A.1) and the water byelaws (see A.2).

The following factors should be taken into account in selecting materials used in a water service:

   a) effect on water quality;

   b) vibration, stress or settlement;

   c) internal water pressure;

   d) internal and external temperatures;

   e) internal and external corrosion;

   f) compatibility of different materials;

   g) ageing, fatigue, durability and other mechanical factors;

   h) permeation.

Materials with a lesser durability than those recommended in this standard may be adequate where the use is for a temporary purpose during a period not exceeding 3 months.

In consultation with the water supplier, consideration should be given to the character of the water supply taking account of any anticipated future changes, and its effect on the choice of materials.

The influence on water quality of the materials used in the construction of the water service installation, and of those in contact with the installation, is dealt with in 2.6.

Internal corrosion leading to premature failure of metal pipes may occur with certain waters. External corrosion of pipes and fittings laid below ground may be a serious local problem depending on the particular ground conditions. Protection by means of a lining internally or coating externally or by using a corrosion resistant material should be considered. (The water supplier may be able to advise on the choice of an effective lining or coating material.)

Careful consideration should be given to how particular materials or products are likely to react in the long term in hot water installations. Ageing, creep and fatigue are important factors when using plastic materials.

1.4.2 Lead

No pipe or other water fitting or storage cistern made from lead or internally lined with lead shall be used in new installations.

Pipework shall not be connected to existing lead pipework without protection against galvanic corrosion.

Repairs to existing lead services shall be by replacement with other materials.

Solders for jointing shall be lead-free.

COMMENTARY AND RECOMMENDATIONS ON 1.4.2

In areas where the water is plumbosolvent, the use of lead components can result in increased lead contamination. (See 2.6.2.1.)

© BSI 1997

1.4.3 Copper

1.4.3.1 Copper tube shall conform to BS 2871 : Part 1. Copper tube fittings shall conform to BS 864.

Copper shall not be connected to other metals without protection against galvanic corrosion.

COMMENTARY AND RECOMMENDATIONS ON 1.4.3.1

It is strongly recommended that independent quality assurance certification of such tube should be obtained.

Copper is, in general, resistant to corrosion and is suitable for hot and cold water applications. Where supply waters are capable of dissolving an undue amount of copper such that either:

a) unacceptable green staining is produced; or

b) deposition of copper onto aluminium or zinc surfaces promotes galvanic attack;

consideration should be given to the use of water treatment or alternative materials.

1.4.3.2 In districts where pitting corrosion of copper cylinders occurs (e.g. where there is hard or moderately hard, deep well water) cylinders shall be fitted with protector rods.

COMMENTARY AND RECOMMENDATIONS ON 1.4.3.2

Protector rods should be fitted during manufacture.

1.4.4 Copper alloys

Copper alloy fittings shall conform to BS 864.

Fittings for use with copper tube laid in the ground shall be resistant or immune to dezincification and where compression fittings are used these shall be manipulative type B fittings conforming to BS 864 : Part 2. Where it is known that the local supply water is capable of causing dezincification, or where distribution systems might introduce such water, or any doubt exists, fittings (except draw off fittings) manufactured from alloys subject to dezincification shall not be used.

COMMENTARY AND RECOMMENDATIONS ON 1.4.4

Copper cannot corrode by dezincification and other recommended materials are the gunmetals or the special brasses inhibited and treated to be highly resistant to this form of corrosion. For alloys in the latter category a specific test of dezincification resistance is included as an appendix to BS 2872 and BS 2874. For ease of identification, fittings manufactured from dezincification resistant brasses capable of passing the test procedures in BS 2872 and BS 2874 are marked with the recognized dezincification symbol CR.

Gunmetal fittings are immune to dezincification.

1.4.5 Stainless steel

Stainless steel tubing shall conform to BS 4127.

Stainless steel tubes shall not be joined by soft solder.

COMMENTARY AND RECOMMENDATIONS ON 1.4.5

Although mixed copper and stainless steel systems can be used, small copper to large stainless steel areas should be avoided, e.g. copper pipes into a large stainless steel tank.

Joining should be made using stainless steel or copper capillary or compression fittings (see 2.6.2).

Joining of stainless steel tubes by adhesive bonding may only be used where the water temperature does not exceed 85 °C.

The water byelaws preclude the use of adhesive jointing of metal pipes where the pipes are laid underground, enclosed in a chase or duct or in any other position where access is difficult.

1.4.6 Steel

1.4.6.1 When carbon steel is used the installer shall ensure that the degree of any protection provided against corrosion is appropriate for the particular conditions of internal water quality and external installation.

COMMENTARY AND RECOMMENDATIONS ON 1.4.6.1

When used above ground for distributing pipes from a storage cistern, steel tube should be medium grade in accordance with BS 1387 and protected against corrosion.

1.4.6.2 Galvanized steel tube shall be joined only by screwed connections. Where it is necessary to change direction pre-formed bends shall be used.

COMMENTARY AND RECOMMENDATIONS ON 1.4.6.2

Galvanized tubes offer only marginal protection against corrosion. Welded or brazed joints should not be used because this would damage the galvanizing.

1.4.7 Plastics

Installations above ground shall accommodate thermal movement. Plastics pipes shall not be installed close to those sources of heat which would impair their performance.

Plastics pipework for hot water systems shall be capable of withstanding a temperature of 100 °C at the maximum working pressure for 1 h.

COMMENTARY AND RECOMMENDATIONS ON 1.4.7

Coefficients of expansion for plastics pipes are greater than those for metal pipes, but this is not generally a problem where pipes are buried. The use and installation of unplasticized polyvinylchloride (PVC-U) pipes should be in accordance with CP 312 : Part 2 and specific attention is drawn to the amendment relating to surge pressures.

Pipe should be in accordance with BS 3505 and the solvent cements to be used with the pipe should be in accordance with BS 4346.

Below ground and in confined locations above ground, mechanical joints should be used in preference to solvent cement joints due to the difficulty in making satisfactory solvent cement joints in such adverse conditions. Where mechanical joints are made with copper alloy fittings these should be dezincification resistant or immune. Where there is adequate access, in positions above ground, solvent cement joints can be used.

As PVC-U pipes become increasingly brittle with reducing temperatures, particular care should be taken in handling them at temperatures below 5 °C.

The use and installation of polyethylene (PE) pipelines for the supply of drinking water should be in accordance with CP 312 : Part 3. Requirements for pipes are specified in BS 1972 (above ground use), BS 6437 (general purposes) and BS 6572 (below ground use, up to size 63). Copper alloy compression fittings for use with PE pipe should be in accordance with BS 864 : Part 3 and joints should conform to BS 5114.

PE cold water storage cisterns in accordance with BS 4213 are suitable for storage and expansion purposes.

Propylene copolymer (PP) cannot be solvent welded. Pipe for drinking water use should conform to series 1 of BS 4991.

Cold water storage cisterns in PP conforming to BS 4213 are suitable for storage and expansion purposes.

Floats in PP for float-operated valves should conform to BS 2456.

Fittings, mostly terminal water fittings, made from acetal are suitable for cold (including potable) and most hot water applications. Jointing carried out by mechanical or push-fit methods is suitable.

Taps conforming to BS 5413 and float-operated valves conforming to BS 1212 : Part 3 are suitable.

Pipes and fittings made from cross-linked polyethylene (PE-X) conforming to BS 7291 : Parts 1 and 3, are suitable for cold and hot water applications.

PE-X cannot be solvent welded. Jointing carried out by mechanical or push-fit methods is suitable using fittings supplied for this purpose.

Pipes and fittings made from polybutylene (PB), conforming to BS 7291 : Parts 1 and 2, are suitable for cold and hot water applications. The material is suitable where resistance to freezing temperatures and abrasion is required.

PB cannot be solvent welded. Jointing by push-fit mechanical joints, or by thermal fusion is suitable.

Pipes and fittings made from chlorinated polyvinyl chloride (PVC-C) conforming to BS 7291: Parts 1 and 4, are suitable for cold and hot water applications. Jointing by solvent welding, screwed joints or unions is suitable.

Plastics pipework systems for pressure applications are not automatically inter-compatible, and there are no specifications in British Standards for connector dimensions or methods of achieving a joint. It is recommended that plastics pipework systems should be comprised of a proprietary system package with third party approval.

1.4.8 Coating and lining materials

No pipe, pipe fitting or storage cistern intended for conveying or storing water shall be lined or coated internally with coal tar or any substance that includes coal tar.

COMMENTARY AND RECOMMENDATIONS ON 1.4.8

See 2.6.2. BS 5493 : 1977 gives recommendations for the protective coating of iron and steel structures, including pipes, fittings and cisterns. This should be consulted where detailed guidance is required. BS 5493 : 1977 deals with non-saline water and is applicable to domestic water installations. Typical times to first maintenance, general descriptions of recommended coatings and their thicknesses are given. Other tables give more detailed information about the coating systems. Of particular relevance is note (n) to table 3, which concerns fittings used with drinking water.

Internal protection of steel pipes should be in accordance with clause 33 of BS 534 : 1990.

1.4.9 The materials of elastomeric sealing rings in contact with drinking water shall conform to the requirements of types W, H or S of BS 2494. Reference should be made to **2.6.2.1**.

© BSI 1997

Section 2. Design considerations

2.1 Initial procedures

2.1.1 Preliminary investigations

The following factors shall be accounted for in the design:

a) the water supplier's requirements;

b) the estimated daily consumption and the maximum and average flow rates required, together with the estimated time of peak flow;

c) the location of the available supply;

d) the quality, quantity and pressure required and the available pressures at various times during a typical day;

e) the cold water storage capacity required;

f) the likelihood of ground subsidence due to mining activities or any other reason;

g) the likelihood of contamination of the site.

COMMENTARY AND RECOMMENDATIONS ON 2.1.1

Where water is to be supplied by a public water supplier all the byelaws of that undertaker are to be conformed to. Byelaws apply whenever the work involves either a new service or the modification or disconnection of existing services. Subject to any express byelaw provisions to the contrary, existing services that conform to the byelaws applicable at the time of their installation need not be updated to conform to current byelaws.

2.1.2 Design

The installation shall be designed to avoid waste, undue consumption, misuse and contamination and to ensure continued conformance to the water byelaws see **A.2** throughout its useful life without an uneconomic maintenance requirement. The installation shall be designed to avoid the trapping of air during filling and the formation of air locks during operation. Where necessary venting valves shall be fitted.

COMMENTARY AND RECOMMENDATIONS ON 2.1.2

The design of the system should include provision not only for the appliances connected to it but also where reasonable, and practicable to do so, for additional appliances that are likely to be installed in the future.

Hot and cold water temperatures should be reached at all points in the system after a maximum period of 1 min running at full flow. To prevent bacteriological contamination the water service should be designed and installed so that cold water is stored and distributed at as low a temperature as possible below 20 °C. Bacteriological contamination is aggravated in buildings with multiple occupancy. The temperature of stored hot water should be in the range 60 °C to 65 °C (see 2.3.1) and the temperature of distributed hot water should be greater than 50 °C.

Guidance on legionnaires' disease is contained in 2.6.4 (also see [2] to [6].

2.1.3 Extensions

Any extension to existing systems shall depend upon their capacity for extension and current water byelaws (see **A.2**).

COMMENTARY AND RECOMMENDATIONS ON 2.1.3

If the existing supply is part of a common supply pipe, i.e. the supply pipe serves several properties, the water supplier may require a separate service pipe to be provided. Where properties are being supplied with a new service from a water supplier's main, it is strongly advised that a separate service pipe should be provided wherever feasible and the supplier will normally require this.

2.1.4 Water mains

Where there is no water main available to serve the premises or the existing main is inadequate to provide a satisfactory supply, the water supplier shall be requested to lay new mains or extend an existing main, or an alternative water supply shall be arranged.

COMMENTARY AND RECOMMENDATIONS ON 2.1.4

Full information about proposals should be furnished as early as possible to the water supplier. Site plans should be supplied showing the layout of roads, footpaths, buildings and boundaries. The work programme should take into account the fact that the supplier will not normally lay a main until at least the line and level of the kerb are permanently established on site.

2.1.5 Water from a private supply shall not access other supplier's mains.

2.1.6 Ground movement

In designing pipe layout, precautions shall be taken to minimize the effects of ground movement on the pipes and fittings.

COMMENTARY AND RECOMMENDATIONS ON 2.1.6

Ground movement may occur due to underground mining operations, natural movements of the earth's strata or movement of superficial deposits. These movements may occur in both the horizontal and vertical planes and will vary in magnitude over the affected area. The effects of under-mining can be predicted with reasonable accuracy by the surveyor of the responsible company who should be consulted for advice on precautionary measures to be adopted.

Movement of superficial deposits may be due to seasonal swelling and shrinkage, settlement (especially where fibrous organic soils are encountered) or to slope stability failures. An appreciation of ground conditions existing along the line of a proposed construction should be gained by site investigation so as to enable an assessment of likely movement to be made.

The extent of movements of superficial deposits can only be assessed by consideration of the findings of a site investigation.

© BSI 1997

Where ground is liable to movement a suitable type of pipework should be used to minimize the risk of damage. Where the pipes or the joints are not sufficiently flexible to accommodate movement in pipelines laid in recently disturbed ground, continuous longitudinal support should be provided.

In selecting the type of pipe or storage cistern, components of brittle materials should be more carefully protected from movement than those of materials containing some inherent flexibility. Provision for change in length of pipelines can be made by the use of telescopic joints whilst angular deflections should be compensated by the use of flexible type joints. The continuity of gradient towards washouts and air valves could be affected by subsidence and therefore when such a situation could occur provision should be made to support pipelines and to ensure reasonable gradients between high and low points on the pipeline. Pipes passing through walls should be free to deflect and in the case of outer walls telescopic joints are recommended. Where a capacity to compensate for compression in such a joint is necessary, the spigot should not be fully pushed home.

2.1.7 Assessment of the site for contamination

Where pipes are to be laid in the ground an assessment of the soil shall be made to detect any contamination (see **2.6.2.2**)

COMMENTARY AND RECOMMENDATIONS ON 2.1.7

In making an assessment of a site, advice should be sought from the local authority, the site owner and the water supplier.

2.1.8 Pipework external to the building

Pipework shall be installed with protection from damage by frost or traffic loads and vibration.

COMMENTARY AND RECOMMENDATION ON 2.1.8

The normal minimum cover for protecting underground pipework against frost damage is achieved by laying pipework at a depth of at least 0.75 m. This may have to be increased to avoid frost damage, obstructions and/or damage from traffic, to a maximum of 1.35 m. (see 2.7 for details on frost protection.)

The following recommendations should be carried out where practicable:

a) no pipework should be laid under surfaced footpaths or drives;

b) the underground service pipe should be laid at right angles to the main;

c) the underground service pipe should be laid in approximately straight lines to facilitate location for repairs but with slight deviations to allow for minor ground movements. Where access for repair or replacement may be difficult, consideration should be given to the provision of some form of duct or sleeve.

External pipework should be located above ground only in exceptional circumstances. It should be lagged with waterproof insulation material in accordance with 2.7.3 and provision should be made for draining of all water from such lengths of pipe in frosty weather through a drain tap, which should not be buried in the ground or so placed that its outlet is in danger of being flooded.

2.1.9 Design consultation

Consultations shall take place with the designer of the building, the building owner or his agent, the water supplier and all other public and private utilities, highway and local authorities, landowners and others involved.

Notices and applications shall be completed and submitted by stipulated times.

Whenever other services are in close proximity to the water service pipes, any byelaws, regulations and requirements of all undertakers concerned shall be ascertained and observed.

Where it is necessary to open the highway or ground for pipe laying or other works, the necessary notices, drawings, documents and applications for consent shall be lodged with the highway authority, public utility undertakers, landowners and any other interested parties as early as possible.

COMMENTARY AND RECOMMENDATIONS ON 2.1.9

The installer should be provided with working drawings of the water services showing clearly the precise location of all pipe runs, indicating the method of ducting to be employed where appropriate, the location and full description of all appliances, valves and all other fittings, methods of fixing, protection and all other information which may be required to enable him to construct the work satisfactorily.

The drawings or an accompanying specification should set out clearly any precautions to be taken against frost, corrosion, bursting, expansion and contraction, contamination, noise, damage due to earth movement or any other damage, any consultation required with other public utilities or subcontractors and any notice to be served before or during the execution of the work.

In respect of all legal requirements, in particular highways, attention is drawn to the terms of the New Roads and Street Works Act 1991 (see A.3).

Where possible, the point of entry of the water service should be arranged to facilitate the equipotential bonding of incoming metallic services to the main electrical earth terminal as near as is practical to their point of entry into the premises.

© BSI 1997

The routing and laying of all services should be co-ordinated to ensure that they are laid in an orderly sequence, to the required line and level and at the appropriate time. A programme should be agreed that takes into consideration the method of construction to be employed, the sequence of hand-over of the buildings, the undertaker's method of working, the size of the services and the position of the incoming services to the site relative to the area to be developed.

In addition to gas, electricity and telephone, other services could include oil pipelines, television relay cables, district heating systems and drainage connections (see National Joint Utilities Group Publication No.6 [7]).

2.2 Cold water services

2.2.1 General

2.2.1.1 The cold water service shall be designed to provide cold water at the point of use in the quantity required by the user, and at a temperature below 20 °C. Except under the circumstances described below, drinking water directly from the supply pipe shall be provided at the kitchen sink in every dwelling. Drinking water is also required at places of work in accordance with the Workplace (Health, Safety and Welfare) Regulations made under the Health and Safety at Work etc. Act 1974 (see **A.4**). Because any cold tap is likely to be used for drinking water, all such taps not connected directly to the supplier's pipe shall be supplied from a storage cistern which is protected in accordance with **2.2.3**.

Where draw-off fittings are above the height to which the water supplier is able or obliged to supply, e.g. in multi-storey buildings, the drinking water tap shall be supplied from a storage cistern that is protected in accordance with **2.2.3** or from a drinking water header from a boosted supply.

Pipe runs to cold water taps within buildings shall not follow the routes of space heating or hot water pipes or pass through heated areas such as airing cupboards or, where local proximity is unavoidable, the hot and cold pipes shall be insulated from each other.

COMMENTARY AND RECOMMENDATIONS ON 2.2.1.1

The insulation requirements given in table 8 will normally give adequate protection against heat gain in pipes and cisterns. In situations where water is likely to remain static for long periods at high temperatures, such as little used taps in plant rooms, actual insulation requirements should be determined by calculation.

2.2.1.2 No drinking water point shall be installed at the end of a long pipe from which only small volumes of water are drawn or water is drawn infrequently.

COMMENTARY AND RECOMMENDATIONS ON 2.2.1.2

Attention is drawn to the Workplace (Health, Safety and Welfare) Regulations 1992 (see A.4) with respect to drinking water provision in office and other commercial buildings.

Drinking water points should be located in areas intended for the preparation of food and for its consumption in addition to rooms provided for beverage making. Where beverage making facilities are not provided, drinking water points should be sited in the vicinity of, but not inside, toilets. Nevertheless, a drinking water fountain may be installed within a toilet area but it should be sited as far away as possible from WCs and urinals and should be of the shrouded nozzle type discharging above the spillover level of the bowl (see BS 6465 : Part 1).

To reduce the risk of stagnation the layout of pipework should be arranged, where possible, so that fittings downstream of a drinking water point have a high demand.

2.2.1.3 The design and method of installation of every tap shall conform to the backflow protection requirements of **2.6.3**.

COMMENTARY AND RECOMMENDATIONS ON 2.2.1.3

In order to enable buckets and similar utensils to be filled, the outlet of the kitchen tap should be not less than 275 mm above the bottom of the sink. To guard against backflow the outlet of such a tap should be designed to make the connection of a hose difficult.

2.2.1.4 Any ion exchange water softeners shall be installed downstream of the supply to the drinking water taps (see figure 1).

Pipework shall be provided to bypass a water softener in the event of malfunction or for the purpose of maintenance.

COMMENTARY AND RECOMMENDATIONS ON 2.2.1.4

Over softening of the water increases the potential for metal dissolution, especially plumbosolvency. If lead pipe exists downstream of the water softener specialist advice should be sought.

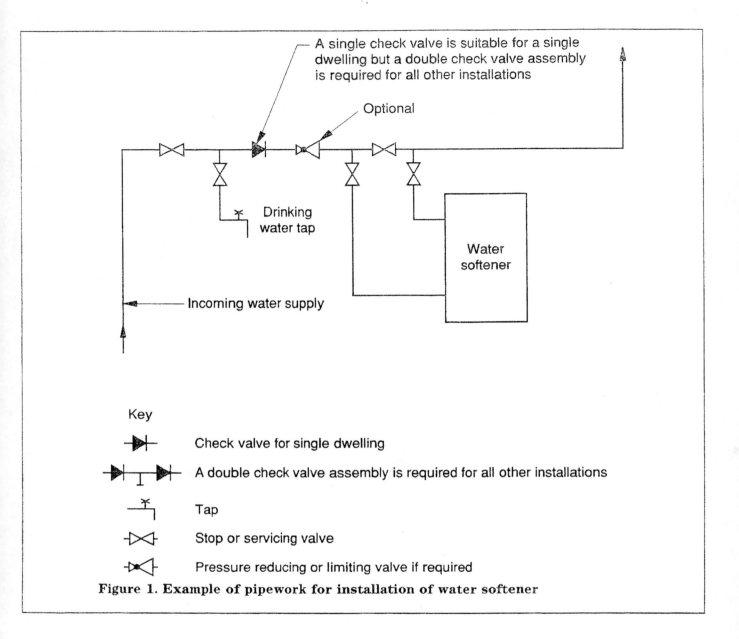

Figure 1. Example of pipework for installation of water softener

© BSI 1997

2.2.2 Type of system

2.2.2.1 The distribution system shall conform to the requirements of the water supplier.

COMMENTARY AND RECOMMENDATIONS ON 2.2.2.1

A choice of cold water supply system might not be available if the water supplier exercises powers to require cold water storage. In any case, considerations of pressure and reliability of supply, particularly where dwellings are located at the extremity of mains distribution system, should be studied.

    a) Characteristics of supply via a storage cistern:

        1) availability of a reserve of water for use in case of interruption of the mains supply;

        2) additional protection of the mains from contamination;

        3) reduced risk of water-hammer and reduced noise from outlets, but additional noise generated by the float-operated valve controlling the water supply to the cistern;

        4) a constant low pressure with reduced risk of leakage and which is suitable for mixer fittings in conjunction with low pressure (vented) hot water supply, but the pressure available is usually insufficient for some types of taps and may not be sufficient for satisfactory showering in the absence of a booster pump;

        5) risk of frost damage;

        6) space occupied and cost of storage cistern, structural support and additional pipework;

        7) need to ensure that the cistern is continuously protected against the ingress of any contaminant.

    b) Characteristics of supply directly from a water main:

        1) smaller pipes may be used in most cases except for the service pipe which may need to be larger than the supply pipe to a storage cistern;

        2) the higher pressure that is usually available is more suitable for instantaneous type shower heaters, hose taps and for mixer fittings used in conjunction with a high pressure (unvented) hot water supply;

        3) where single outlet mixer fittings are used measures to prevent backflow may be necessary when used in conjunction with a low pressure (vented) hot water supply.

In some cases a combination of the two methods or supply may be the best arrangement. In a dwelling, for example, the ground floor cold outlets and any outside tap could be supplied under mains pressure while all other cold water outlets could be fed from a storage cistern.

2.2.2.2 Systems in buildings other than dwellings

For buildings other than dwellings, the method of supply shall be related to the size and usage of the building and the number of appliances to be served.

COMMENTARY AND RECOMMENDATIONS ON 2.2.2.2

In the case of small buildings where the water consumption is likely to be comparable to that of a dwelling house, the options stated in 2.2.2.1 should be considered. For larger buildings, it will be acceptable for all water, except drinking water, to be supplied indirectly via a storage cistern or cisterns.

Drinking water should be taken directly from the water supplier's main wherever practicable or, when circumstances dictate otherwise, from a cistern protected in accordance with 2.2.3.1.

2.2.2.3 Pumped systems

The prior written consent of the water supplier shall be obtained before a pump is connected in or to a supply pipe.

COMMENTARY AND RECOMMENDATIONS ON 2.2.2.3

Where the available pressure is insufficient to supply the whole of a building and the water supplier is unable to increase the supply pressure in the supplier's mains, consideration should be given to installing a pumped system.

When deciding on the method of pumping and on the siting of break tanks and pumps, consideration should be given to the use of such pressure as may be available in the mains supply. In all systems, precautions have to be taken to ensure that backflow does not occur from the distribution pipework and pumping plant (see 2.6.1.3 and 2.6.3).

2.2.3 Storage cisterns

2.2.3.1 General

2.2.3.1.1 Drinking water storage cisterns and covers shall not impart taste, colour, odour or toxicity to the water, nor promote or foster microbial growth (see **2.6**). Any cistern from which water for domestic purposes may be drawn shall be watertight and shall be:

a) fitted with a rigid, close fitting and securely fixed cover which is not airtight but excludes light and insects from the cistern, fits closely around any vent pipe, made of materials which will not shatter or fragment when broken and will not contaminate any water which condenses on its underside;

b) where necessary, lined or coated with a material suitable for use in contact with drinking water;

c) where necessary, insulated against heat and frost;

d) supplied from a supply pipe from the water supplier's mains or from a pump drawing water from a cistern which is also a watertight closed vessel similarly equipped and supplied as above;

e) when of capacity greater than 1000 l, so constructed that the interior can be readily inspected and cleaned, and the inlet control valve adjusted and maintained without having to remove the cover or the whole of any cover which is in two or more parts; and

f) provided with warning and overflow pipes, as appropriate (see **2.2.4**), which are constructed and arranged to exclude insects.

COMMENTARY AND RECOMMENDATIONS ON 2.2.3.1.1

Table 1 gives recommendations for storage capacities related to various types of use but these are to be regarded as a guide only. The water supplier should be consulted regarding any particular requirements it may have in this matter.

In determining the total capacity of cold water storage in the premises concerned, account should be taken of:

a) the need to prevent stagnation by ensuring that water is held in storage for as short a time as possible; and

b) the requirements of any associated water-using fittings and appliances, particularly where supply interruptions could cause damage to property or inconvenience to the consumer.

The probable pattern of water use (draw-off rates and their durations) should be determined and account taken of any local conditions of low or reduced mains pressures likely to affect cistern refilling at times of peak demand.

In single dwellings it is usual for storage cisterns supplying cold water fittings only to have a capacity of 100 l to 150 l, and double this capacity if supplying all water outlets, hot and cold.

Alternatively, where a constant supply at adequate pressure is a statutory requirement, a maximum capacity of 80 l per person normally resident should prove satisfactory. A larger capacity based on 130 l per person would be appropriate where cistern refilling normally takes place only during the night hours.

The water supplier should be consulted before finalising cistern capacity to hotels, hostels, office premises (with or without canteen facilities), schools (day and boarding) and other substantial establishments.

Separation of capacity among two or more cisterns should facilitate water distribution, but inlets and outlets should be located to prevent short-circuiting within the cisterns.

Table 1. Recommended minimum storage of cold water for domestic purposes (hot and cold outlets)

Type of building or occupation	Minimum storage l
Hostel	90 per bed space
Hotel	200 per bed space
Office premises:	
with canteen facilities	45 per employee
without canteen facilities	40 per employee
Restaurant	7 per meal
Day school:	
nursery	15 per pupil
primary	
secondary	20 per pupil
technical	
Boarding school	90 per pupil
Children's home or residential nursery	135 per bed space
Nurses' home	120 per bed space
Nursing or convalescent home	135 per bed space

© BSI 1997

2.2.3.1.2 The material of a cistern shall be corrosion resistant or shall be coated internally with an approved non-toxic corrosion resistant material conforming to BS 6920 : Parts 1,2 and 3. The cistern and its cover shall be designed to have sufficient strength to operate without undue deformation.

2.2.3.1.3 The cistern shall be supported on a firm level base which is capable of withstanding the weight of the cistern when filled with water to the rim. Every plastics cistern shall be supported on a flat rigid platform fully supporting the bottom of the cistern over the whole of its area.

2.2.3.1.4 Access shall be provided as described in **2.8.4**. Space shall be provided under and around the cistern for maintenance and the outlet of any overflow pipe shall be above outside ground or flood level.

2.2.3.1.5 Every cistern providing drinking water shall be protected from ingress of contaminants. Cisterns sunk in the ground shall have special measures to detect leakage.

Where the ground water table dictates, buried cisterns shall be anchored to prevent them lifting when empty or partially filled.

2.2.3.1.6 Except for interconnected cisterns arranged to store water at the same water level, every pipe supplying water to a cistern shall be fitted with a float-operated valve or some other equally effective device to control the inflow of water and maintain it at the required level. The inlet control device shall be suitable for the particular application.

When a float-operated valve is used it shall either:

a) conform to BS 1212 : Parts 1, 2, 3 or 4 and be used with a float conforming to BS 1968 or BS 2456 of the correct size corresponding to the length of the lever arm and the water supply pressure; or

b) where any other float-operated valve or other level control device is used, it shall conform to the performance requirements of BS 1212 : Parts 1, 2, 3 or 4 where applicable to the circumstances of its use and shall be clearly marked with the water pressure, temperature and other characteristics for which it is intended to be used (see also **2.6.3**).

Every float-operated valve shall be securely fixed to the cistern it supplies and where necessary braced to prevent the thrust of the float causing the valve to move and so affect the water level at which it closes. This water level shall be at least 25 mm below the lowest point of the warning pipe connection or, if no warning pipe is fitted, at least 50 mm below the lowest point of the lowest overflow pipe connection.

2.2.3.1.7 All cold water distributing pipes from cisterns shall be connected at the lowest point on the cistern.

2.2.3.1.8 Connections to distributing pipes feeding hot water apparatus shall be set at a level at least 25 mm above connections to pipes feeding cold water outlets.

COMMENTARY AND RECOMMENDATIONS ON 2.2.3.1.8

This requirement will minimize the risk of scalding from mixer fittings such as showers, should the water supply fail.

2.2.3.2 Large cisterns

Cisterns over 1000 l capacity shall additionally conform to the following requirements.

To avoid interruption of the water supply when carrying out repairs or maintenance, the cistern shall be provided with compartments or a standby cistern.

A washout pipe shall not be connected to a drain but may be arranged to discharge into open air at least 150 mm above a drain if required.

COMMENTARY AND RECOMMENDATIONS ON 2.2.3.2

A washout pipe should be provided flush with the bottom of the cistern at its lowest point. Where practicable, the floor of the cistern should be laid to a slight fall to the washout pipe for cleaning purposes. The washout pipe outlet should be controlled by a suitable fullway valve and blanked off with a plug or flange when not in use.

Sometimes, particularly in the case of a complex of buildings, because of the larger volume of storage required or to provide the necessary head, it may be necessary to support the cistern in an independent structure outside the building(s). Although such a storage facility is often referred to as a tank or water tower, it is, by definition, a cistern.

Cisterns mounted outside buildings, whether fixed to the building itself or supported on an independent structure, should be enclosed in a well ventilated, but draughtproof, housing constructed to prevent ingress of birds, animals, and insects, but providing access to the interior of the cistern by authorized persons for inspection and maintenance. Ventilation openings should be screened by a corrosion-resistant mesh with a maximum aperture size of 0.65 mm.

2.2.4 Warning and overflow pipes

Every cistern of capacity (if filled to the level at which water just starts to flow through any overflow pipe) up to 1000 l shall be fitted with a warning pipe, and no other overflow pipe. Cisterns of capacity exceeding 1000 l shall be fitted with one or more overflow pipes. For capacities up to 5000 l the lowest overflow pipe shall be a warning pipe. For capacities over 5000 l but not greater than 10 000 l, either the lowest overflow pipe shall be a warning pipe, or a device shall be fitted that indicates when the water in the cistern reaches a level that is at least 50 mm below the lowest point of the lowest overflow pipe connection. For capacities greater than 10 000 l, either the lowest overflow pipe shall be a warning pipe or a device shall be fitted that gives an audible or visual alarm when the water reaches the level of overflowing and which acts independently of the normal service inlet control valve.

Overflow and warning pipes shall be made of rigid, corrosion resistant material; no flexible hose shall be connected to or form part of any overflow or warning pipe. When a single overflow pipe is fitted its bore shall be greater than that of the inlet pipe to the cistern and in no case shall any warning pipe be less than 19 mm internal diameter.

No warning or overflow pipe shall rise in level outside the cistern.

Every warning pipe shall discharge water immediately the water in the cistern reaches the overflowing level and shall discharge in a conspicuous position, preferably outside the building where this is appropriate.

It is permissible for the separate warning pipes from several storage or WC flushing cisterns to be combined into one outlet, provided that the source of any overflow may be readily identified and that any overflow from one cistern cannot discharge into another. No warning pipe shall be arranged to discharge into a WC pan via the flush pipe.

COMMENTARY AND RECOMMENDATIONS ON 2.2.4

The overflow pipe or pipes should be able to carry away all the water which is discharged into the cistern in the event of the inlet control device becoming defective, without the water level reaching the spill-over level of the cistern or submerging the discharge opening of the inlet pipe or valve.

Where overflow and warning pipes discharge through the external wall of a building they should be arranged so as to prevent the inward flow of cold air by turning down the warning pipe into the cistern and below the water line except where this could interfere with the operation of the flushing mechanism or float-operated valve in a WC flushing cistern.

2.2.5 Stopvalves

2.2.5.1 Stopvalves fitted to supply pipes below ground shall conform to BS 2580 or BS 5433 when the pipe is less than 50 mm nominal size, with BS 2580, BS 5163 or BS 5433 when the pipe is 50 mm nominal size, and with BS 5163 when the pipe is greater than 50 mm nominal size. Stopvalves fitted to service pipes above ground shall either conform to the appropriate requirements for stopvalves fitted to supply pipes below ground or, when the pipe is not larger than 50 mm nominal size, to BS 1010 : Part 2 (see table 2).

Table 2. British Standards for stopvalves		
Nominal size of pipe	**British Standard**	
	Above ground	**Below ground**
50 mm or smaller	BS 1010 : Part 2 BS 2580 BS 5433	BS 2580 BS 5433
50 mm or larger	BS 5163	BS 5163

The stopvalve components of composite fittings incorporating stopvalves shall conform to the requirements for stopvalves.

When a stopvalve is installed on an underground pipe it shall be enclosed in a pipe guard under a surface box.

2.2.5.2 In every building or part of a building to which a separately chargeable supply of water is provided and in any premises occupied as a dwelling, whether or not separately charged for a supply of water, a stopvalve shall be provided that controls the whole of the supply to those premises without shutting off the supply to any other premises. This stopvalve shall, so far as is practicable, be installed within the building or premises concerned in an accessible position above floor level and close to the point of entry of the pipe supplying water to that premises, whether this be a supply pipe or a distributing pipe.

In addition, where a common supply or distributing pipe provides water to two or more premises, it shall be fitted with a stopvalve that controls the water supply to all of the premises supplied by that pipe. This stopvalve shall be installed either inside or outside the building in a position to which every occupier of the premises supplied has access.

A stopvalve shall be installed in every pipe supplying water to any structure erected within the curtilage of a building but having no access from the main building. This stopvalve shall be located in the main building as near as practicable to the exit point of the supply pipe to the other structure or if this is not practicable in the other structure itself as near as possible to the entry point of the supply.

© BSI 1997

COMMENTARY AND RECOMMENDATIONS ON 2.2.5.2

In addition to the above requirements, it is often advantageous where a building is divided into separately occupied parts, for the supply to each part to be capable of being shut off by a second stopvalve installed outside that part without shutting off the supply to other parts of the building. The principle on which these requirements and recommendations are based is to provide a ready means of isolating any private or common supply causing damage or nuisance or for the purpose of effecting repairs, replacements or alterations. Any occupier should be able to drain down his supply to avoid frost damage and to shut off his own supply or a supply in unoccupied premises which is causing damage or nuisance by means of a stopvalve under his control or to which he has ready access.

2.2.6 Servicing valves

2.2.6.1 Servicing valves shall be provided and located in accessible positions so as to enable the flow of water to individual or groups of appliances to be controlled and to limit the inconvenience caused by interruption of supply during repairs.

2.2.6.2 A servicing valve shall be protected against unauthorized use. Screwdown servicing valves shall not be of loose washer plate design.

2.2.6.3 A servicing valve shall be fitted upstream of, and as close as practicable to, every float-operated valve or other device used to control the inflow and level of water.

Every pipe taking water from a cistern of capacity exceeding 18 l shall be fitted with a servicing valve near the cistern.

Pipes connecting feed cisterns to primary circuits shall not be fitted with servicing valves where the capacity of the cistern does not exceed 18 l.

COMMENTARY AND RECOMMENDATIONS ON 2.2.6.3

Having regard to the hydraulic resistance of screwdown type valves, it is permissible for copper alloy gatevalves conforming to BS 5154 to be used for this purpose. Specially designed spherical valves are available in the smaller sizes and are well suited for fitting near to single outlet fittings and appliances as servicing valves.

2.2.7 Draining taps

Every pipe which supplies water to a premises shall be fitted with a draining tap and arranged so that when the stopvalve installed according to **2.2.5.2** is closed, and the draining tap is open, the supply pipe downstream of the stopvalve can be drained (see **2.7.5**).

Draining taps shall be fixed over a drain or have provision for discharging the water to the nearest convenient point for disposal. The draining taps on any supply or distributing pipe shall not be buried in the ground or so placed that their outlet is in danger of being flooded.

COMMENTARY AND RECOMMENDATIONS ON 2.2.7

Combined stopvalves and draining taps are a convenient way of providing facilities for draining.

The pipe runs on the downstream of every stopvalve should be arranged so as to drain continuously towards draining taps or draw-off taps at the low points. All cisterns, tanks, cylinders and boilers should be fitted with draining taps unless they can be drained through pipes leading to draining taps or draw-off taps elsewhere; provision should be made for draining both the primary and secondary parts of an indirect hot water cylinder or calorifier. Provision should be made for draining low level pipes such as those laid in ducts under a ground floor.

All draining taps should be capable of being fitted with removable hosepipes unless installed over a drain or discharging into a permanent draining pipe. Where a draining tap is necessarily at such a level or in such a position that complete drainage cannot be obtained, even by the aid of a hosepipe and syphonic action, then a sump that can be emptied by bailing or pumping should be provided to receive the water drained from the tap.

Adequate facilities should be provided to permit entry of air into the system when draining down. Where the taps and float-operated valves in the system are not suitably located for this purpose, special air inlet valves should be fitted in appropriate locations.

When a sump is used it should be arranged so that the water level in it will at all times be kept below the outlet of the drain tap to preserve an air gap and prevent backflow. Similarly, outlets of hoses connected to draining taps should be arranged to discharge freely into the air; at no time should such hose outlets be allowed to become submerged.

For effective draining, it is essential that air enters the pipework freely and draw-off taps, float-operated valves and air inlet valves should be open for this purpose when draining is being carried out. Hot water cylinders are liable to collapse if air cannot enter the system.

Draining taps should be used for draining purposes only. Where a draw-off tap is used for draining the installation, it should not be fitted with a hose unless it has backflow protection as indicated in table 5 and in accordance with the water byelaws (see A.2).

Attention is drawn to the situation where the provision of check valves and double check valve assemblies for backflow prevention at draw off taps, particularly those with flexible hoses, and other equipment may also prevent air entering the system during a draining operation.

© BSI 1997

2.2.8 Revenue meter installations

2.2.8.1 *General*

The consumer shall consult with the water supplier to carry out the installation of a revenue meter, with regard to any requirements concerning the installation additional to those specified in **2.2.8.2** to **2.2.8.5** before work is begun.

COMMENTARY AND RECOMMENDATIONS ON 2.2.8.1

Meters on the incoming supply to a premises, for revenue charging purposes, are usually supplied by the water supplier and sited by agreement between the consumer and the water supplier.

Wherever possible meters should be installed at or near the street boundary of the premises supplied, which is the limit of the responsibility of the water supplier for maintenance of the communication pipe. Where a meter is to be installed near the boundary of a premises, the distance to the public highway should not exceed 10 m. However, in the case of flats and industrial premises or shops in multiple occupation, as well as existing premises opting for a meter for the first time, an internal installation may be necessary and is acceptable provided it registers the whole supply.

The meter should be protected from the risk of damage by shock or vibration induced by the surroundings at the place of installation.

2.2.8.2 *Meters*

Meters shall conform to BS 5728 : Part 1, with suitable connectors to facilitate future meter changes without the use of heat or major disturbance of the pipework.

2.2.8.3 *Bonding*

A suitable conductor shall be installed for bonding between inlet and outlet pipework connections to water meters, water suppliers' stopvalves or other water conveying components in a metal water supply pipe to ensure equipotential bonding applies to any pipework temporarily disconnected for the purpose of removing such components for replacement or maintenance (see **3.1.8** and **4.2.5**).

For dwellings a bond of at least 6 mm² cross-section shall be connected prior to attaching the pipework and shall remain in place following installation.

COMMENTARY AND RECOMMENDATIONS ON 2.2.8.3

These requirements are necessary on both internal and external installations for protection of the installer against electrical fault and for maintenance of the earth connection.

2.2.8.4 *External installations*

2.2.8.4.1 In external meter installations the meter shall be installed below ground in a position accessible for meter reading and changing, with the dial uppermost.

The chamber shall be fitted with a cover marked 'water meter', of sufficient strength to carry the loads to which it may be subjected and fitted with slots or lifting eyes.

Pipes, cables or drains other than the meter pipework shall not pass through the meter chamber.

The chamber shall be sized so that there is ample space available for removing the meter using the necessary hand tools.

Space shall be left for the extraction of bolts from flanges for ready dismantling of joints and no part of the meter assembly shall be built into the walls of the chamber or concreted into the chamber.

The pipe on both sides of the meter assembly shall have a clearance space around it through the wall of the chamber to facilitate exchange of the meter. Where the chamber needs to be watertight, the clearance shall be fitted with a sealing material approved by the water supplier and sufficient length of pipe left inside the pit to facilitate meter exchange.

Pipework on both sides of the meter assembly shall be firmly fixed to prevent movement of any flexible joints within the meter assembly. Nevertheless, such anchorage shall leave sufficient room for connecting and disconnecting the meter making use of the adaptors provided. The meter shall also be supported on the underside so as not to create differential loads between the meter and its connecting pipework.

There shall be a valve which isolates the meter on both the inlet and the outlet.

COMMENTARY AND RECOMMENDATIONS ON 2.2.8.4.1

For housing and other installations where the maximum water requirement does not exceed 3500 l/h the chamber may be constructed of glass reinforced plastics or PVC (see figure 2).

For meters where the water flow exceeds 3500 l/h the chamber should be constructed of brick or concrete.

The clear opening of the surface box should be the same as the internal dimensions of the chamber.

Steel framed, concrete filled covers to chambers are not recommended on account of their weight and their liability to flex causing the concrete to crack and the cover to jam.

© BSI 1997

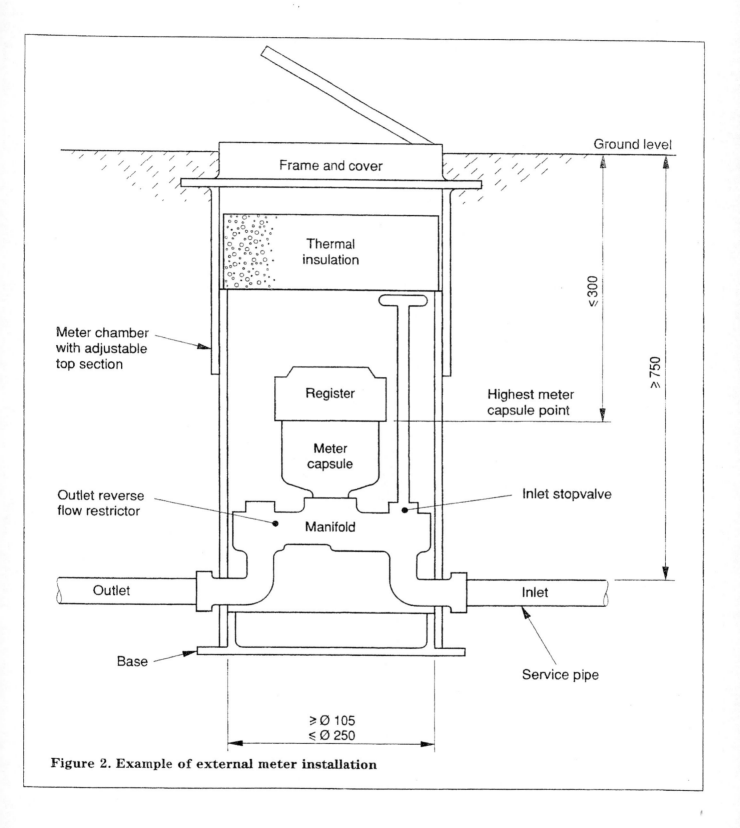

Figure 2. Example of external meter installation

Ground level

Frame and cover

Thermal insulation

Meter chamber with adjustable top section

Register

Highest meter capsule point

Meter capsule

Outlet reverse flow restrictor

Inlet stopvalve

Manifold

Outlet

Inlet

Base

Service pipe

≤ 300

≥ 750

≥ Ø 105
≤ Ø 250

© BSI 1997

2.2.8.4.2 Any stopvalve in a meter chamber shall conform to table 2.

2.2.8.5 *Internal meters*

2.2.8.5.1 Internal meters shall be fixed horizontally or vertically and with the dial not more than 1.5 m above floor level and readily visible for reading.

Where the existing pipework is, or can be, re-positioned so as to be parallel to the wall and is not less than 50 mm away from it, installations shall be as indicated in figure 3.

COMMENTARY AND RECOMMENDATIONS ON 2.2.8.5.1

Where a consumer wishes to limit access to the meter for reading purposes, a remote readout device may be installed if the water supplier agrees.

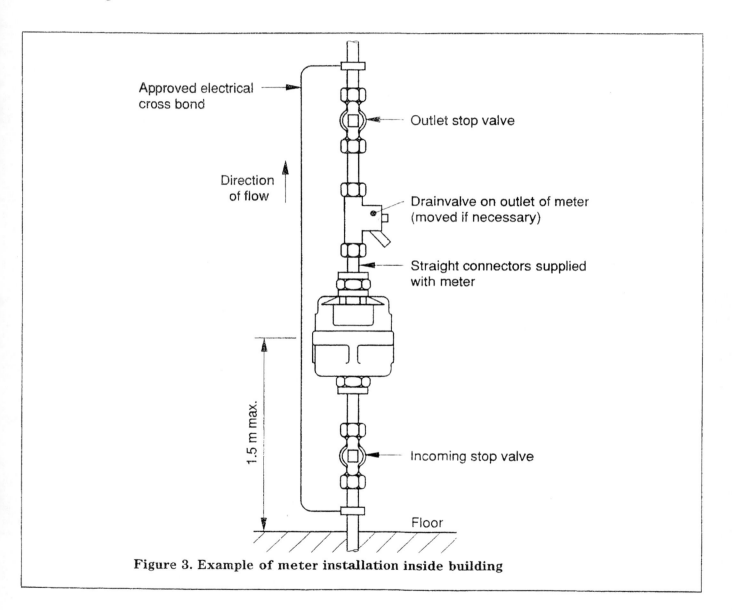

Figure 3. Example of meter installation inside building

© BSI 1997

2.2.8.5.2 Pipework shall be adequately supported, leaving sufficient room for changing the meter with the connections provided.

2.2.8.5.3 The meter shall be installed downstream of the internal stopvalve and as close to it as possible. Where a drain valve is required, in accordance with the byelaws, it shall be installed immediately downstream of the meter.

COMMENTARY AND RECOMMENDATIONS ON 2.2.8.5.3

The length of pipe between the stopvalve and the meter cannot easily be drained and will thus require effective protection against damage from frost in accordance with 2.7.

2.2.8.5.4 A second stopvalve or servicing valve shall be installed downstream of the meter.

2.2.8.5.5 Where the installation of meters in exposed locations, e.g. garages subject to frost, is unavoidable and agreed by the water supplier, adequate insulation in accordance with **2.7.3** shall be provided but not so as to seriously impede reading or changing the meter.

2.2.9 Non-revenue meters

The installation of non-revenue meters shall conform to 2.2.8 except that the water supplier need not be consulted.

2.3 Hot water services

2.3.1 General principles

The hot water service shall be designed to provide hot water at the point of use, in the quantities and at the temperatures required by the user.

COMMENTARY AND RECOMMENDATIONS ON 2.3.1

Under normal conditions the temperature of the stored water should never exceed 65 °C. A stored water temperature of 60 °C is considered sufficient to meet all normal requirements and will minimize deposition of scale in hard water areas. Minimum temperatures are given in 2.1.2.

The design should take account of maintenance, fuel costs, efficiency of the system and the safety of the user. The relevant codes of practice for installation should be used, e.g. BS 5546 for gas installations.

2.3.2 Choice of system

Where the user requirements are not specified, and in particular where the user is not known, as in speculative housing developments for example, an assessment of user needs shall be made on the basis of the size and type of building, experience and convention.

Where a dwelling has only one bathroom it shall be assumed that immediately after filling a bath, some hot water will be required for kitchen use, but a second bath will not be required within 20 min to 30 min. Where a dwelling has two or more bathrooms it shall be assumed that all the installed baths will be filled in succession and that hot water will immediately be required for kitchen use (see figure 4).

COMMENTARY AND RECOMMENDATIONS ON 2.3.2

Data on which this assessment is made should include the following:

Hot water (60 °C) used in dwellings:	*35 l to 45 l per person per day*
Average bath:	*60 l at 60 °C plus*
	40 l at 10 °C
	or 100 l at 40 °C
Shower:	*0.05 l to 0.10 l/s at 40 °C*
Power shower:	*Up to 0.2 l/s at 40 °C*
Wash basin hot tap:	*0.10 l to 0.15 l/s at 40 °C to 60 °C*
Kitchen sink	*0.10 to 0.20 l/s at 60 °C*

NOTE. Although temperatures of 40 °C are quoted above, these are achieved by mixing cold and hot water as required.

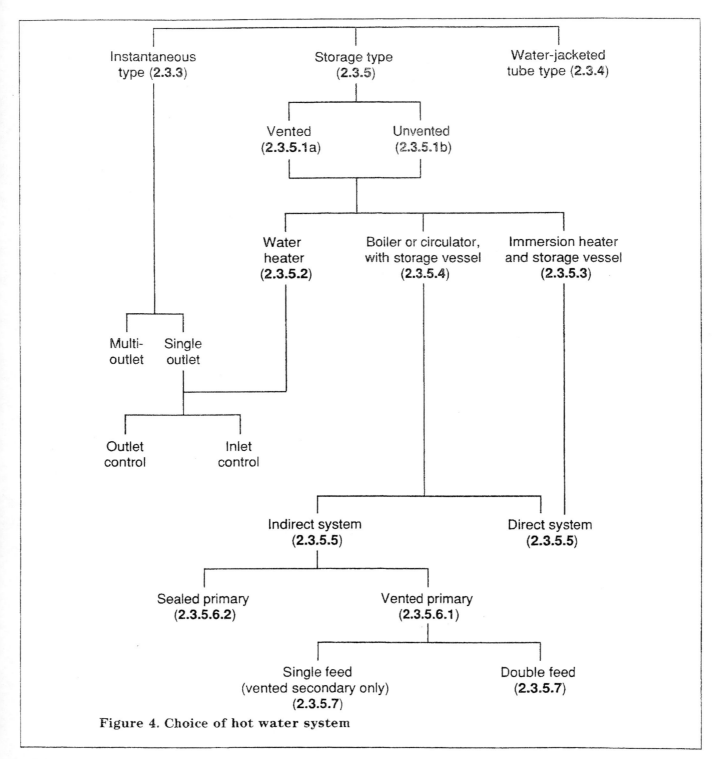

Figure 4. Choice of hot water system

2.3.3 Gas water heaters in bathrooms

Gas-fired instantaneous water heaters installed in bathrooms shall be of the room-sealed type.

2.3.4 Water-jacketed tube heaters

Water-jacketed tube heater installations supplied directly from a supply pipe shall accommodate expansion of water so that there is no discharge from the system except in emergency situations.

© BSI 1997

COMMENTARY AND RECOMMENDATIONS ON 2.3.4

The cold water feed may be from a supply pipe or from a storage cistern. The water drawn for use passes through a heat exchanger in a reservoir of primary water heated by an integral or separate boiler. The size of this reservoir, which in some designs can include the space-heating circuit, the rate of heat input to it and the heat exchanger characteristics determine the amount and rate of flow of hot water that can be provided without unacceptable temperature drop. The primary circuit may be vented or sealed.

The performance characteristics of individual appliances should be ascertained from the manufacturers.

2.3.5 Storage-type hot water systems

2.3.5.1 *Choice of vented or unvented system*

The choice between the vented and the unvented type of installation shall be made in conjunction with the choice of method of cold water supply (see **2.2.2**). Whichever system is installed, it shall conform to the relevant requirements of **2.4**.

COMMENTARY AND RECOMMENDATIONS ON 2.3.5.1

Except for supplies to dual stream fittings, mixing fittings should be supplied with comparable hot and cold water supply pressures.

A summary of the main differences between vented and unvented systems is as follows.

a) Vented systems: vented domestic hot water service systems are fed with cold water from a storage cistern which is situated above the highest outlet to provide the necessary pressure in the system and which accommodates expansion of the water when it is heated. An open vent pipe runs from the top of the hot water storage vessel to a point above the water storage cistern, into which it is arranged to vent. Explosion protection involving no mechanical devices is provided by the open vent and the cistern.

b) Unvented systems: unvented systems can be supplied from a storage cistern, either directly or through a booster pump, but usually from the supply pipe, either directly or via a pressure reducing valve. The main characteristics of unvented systems are as follows.

1) Explosion protection is provided by safety devices.

2) Systems depend upon pressure continuity and the hot water flow cannot be guaranteed if pressures fall.

3) In unvented systems supplied from a supply pipe the absence of a storage cistern may reduce the risk of frost damage to property and removes the source of refill, or float-operated valve noise.

4) The safety aspects of unvented, storage-type hot water systems are subject to the requirements of the building regulations (see A.1).

2.3.5.2 *Storage water heaters*

2.3.5.2.1 *Non-pressure or inlet controlled type*

No hose or other connection shall be made to the outlet of a non-pressure or inlet-controlled storage-type water heater and the outlet shall not be controlled by a valve or tap.

Commentary and recommendations on 2.3.5.2.1

Special taps and mixer taps in which the tap mechanism controls the cold water inlet to the heater while the hot water from the heater is discharged through the tap outlet can be used when specified by the heater manufacturer, provided the tap outlet remains unobstructed.

2.3.5.2.2 *Pressure or outlet controlled type*

The heater shall be suitable for the supply pressure and there shall be appropriate arrangements to accommodate expansion of the heated water.

COMMENTARY AND RECOMMENDATIONS ON 2.3.5.2.2

Many pressure-type water heaters are designed to be supplied from a storage cistern only and will not withstand mains water pressures.

For installations in small dwellings a capacity of 100 l to 150 l is sufficient to provide a hot water supply including a supply to a bath. Heaters designed to take advantage of off-peak electricity tariffs may have a capacity of 200 l or more.

2.3.5.3 *Storage vessel with electric immersion heater*

The storage vessel shall conform to the relevant requirements of **2.6** and shall be corrosion resistant. The immersion heater or heaters shall conform to BS 3456 : Section 2.21; all electrical controls shall conform to BS 3955.

Immersion heaters and controls shall be so located that insertion, removal and adjustment can easily be performed.

The insertion of an immersion heater into the storage vessel of an indirect system provides direct heating so far as the immersion heater is concerned and the safety controls appropriate to a direct system shall be fitted.

COMMENTARY AND RECOMMENDATIONS ON 2.3.5.3

This appliance is site assembled, and it is important to ensure that it is protected against bursting in accordance with 2.4 for a direct system and that any backflow prevention devices required by 2.6 are correctly fitted.

Immersion heaters form a convenient means of providing supplementary water heating in systems combining hot water supply and space heating (see 2.3.5.6).

2.3.5.4 *Boiler heated hot water systems*

Boiler heated hot water systems specified in this standard comprise a hot water storage vessel and an independent heating appliance, a back-boiler associated with an open fire or room heater, a boiler incorporated in a cooker, or a gas-fired circulator.

2.3.5.5 *Direct and indirect systems*

Direct systems shall be designed to achieve gravity circulation between boiler and storage vessel. In hard water areas where scale deposition may obstruct pipes an indirect system shall be used.

An indirect system shall be used when domestic hot water and hot water central heating are supplied by the same boiler. The primary circuit of an indirect system shall either be cistern fed and vented, or be filled and sealed.

Primary circuits shall not be permanently connected to a supply pipe. A temporary connection via a double check valve assembly permanently installed in the primary circuit is permissible for filling, or flushing the primary circuit. Any temporary connection of this kind shall be made only for such time as is necessary to carry out the task in question.

When gravity circulation is required the storage vessel shall be located at a sufficient height above the boiler. Flow and return pipes shall have a route and bore appropriate to the duty required and circulating head available.

COMMENTARY AND RECOMMENDATIONS ON 2.3.5.5

This standard includes direct and indirect, vented and unvented systems. Figures 5 to 8 illustrate the basic differences between direct and indirect, and between vented and unvented systems. These figures are diagrammatic and should not be taken as complete designs; for simplicity, gravity circulation is shown and temperature controls and distribution pipework omitted.

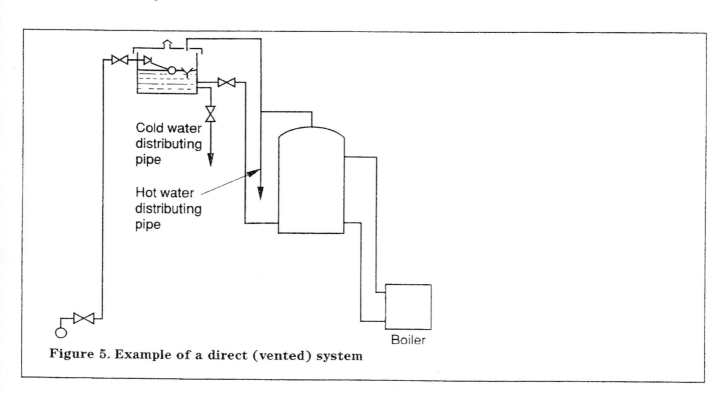

Cold water distributing pipe

Hot water distributing pipe

Boiler

Figure 5. Example of a direct (vented) system

© BSI 1997

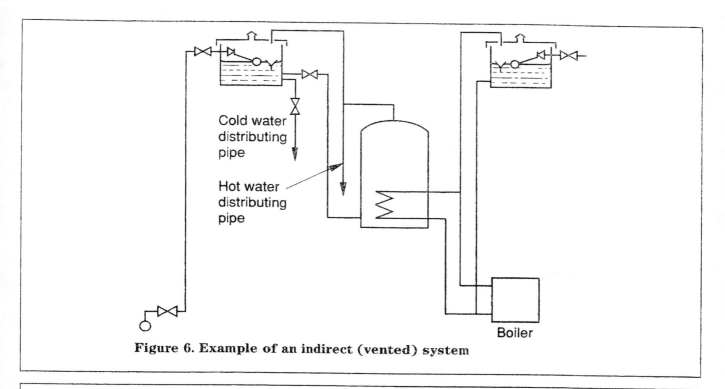

Cold water
distributing
pipe

Hot water
distributing
pipe

Boiler

Figure 6. Example of an indirect (vented) system

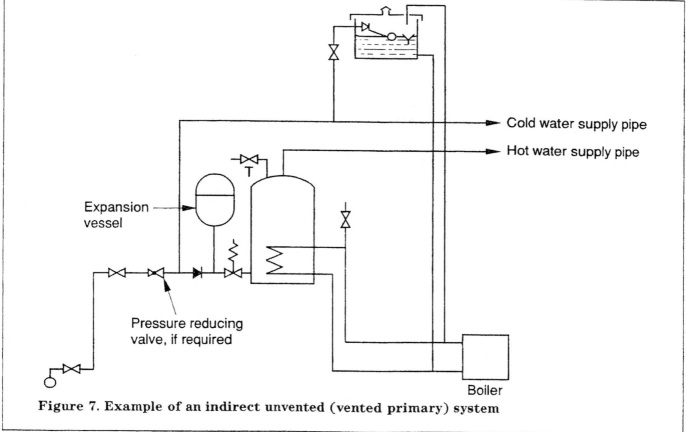

Cold water supply pipe

Hot water supply pipe

Expansion
vessel

Pressure reducing
valve, if required

Boiler

Figure 7. Example of an indirect unvented (vented primary) system

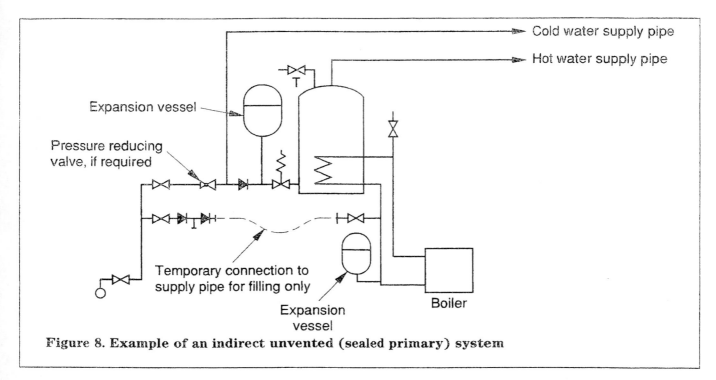

Figure 8. Example of an indirect unvented (sealed primary) system

2.3.5.6 Domestic hot water primary circuits

2.3.5.6.1 *Vented primary circuits*

Vented primary circuits shall have a vent route connecting the flow connection on the boiler to the vent pipe outlet above the expansion cistern and a feed water route from a point near the bottom of the expansion cistern to the return connection on the boiler. Except as specified in this subclause, these routes shall be independent. It is permissible for both these routes to be incorporated in parts of the primary flow and return pipework, but the vent route shall not include any valve, pump or any impediment to flow whatsoever.

Where the design of the primary circuit so dictates, it is permissible to include a circulating pump and its associated isolating valves in the feed water route. A feed and expansion cistern for a double feed primary circuit shall accommodate 4 % expansion of the volume of the water in the circuit. Except for a circulating pump and its associated isolating valves and except for a servicing valve, both fitted only in the circumstances specified in this subclause, the feed water route shall not include any valve, pump or any impediment to flow whatsoever. Where the vent route and water route are combined, the boiler and primary circuit shall have the protection specified in **2.4** for a sealed primary circuit and the combined route shall not include any valve, pump or any impediment to flow.

For domestic installations the vent shall not be less than 19 mm bore (see **2.4.2.3**). Where the vent pipe is not connected to the highest point in the primary circuit, an air release valve shall be installed at that point.

COMMENTARY AND RECOMMENDATIONS ON 2.3.5.6.1

This requirement does not exclude the use of a close-coupled feed and vent where this is installed in accordance with BS 5449. Pipes should be installed to avoid air locks and laid to falls to facilitate draining.

When an installation is designed for combined central and domestic water heating and the central heating circuit includes a circulating pump while the parallel circuit to the primary heater in the hot water storage vessel operates by gravity circulation, the return pipes of the two circuits should be connected to separate connections on the boiler or should be combined by means of an injector type fitting installed near the boiler, unless the manufacturers' instructions specify otherwise.

2.3.5.6.2 *Sealed primary circuits*

Pipes sizes in sealed primary circuits shall conform to the relevant requirements for vented primary circuits specified in **2.3.5.6.1**. In place of the expansion cistern and vent pipe, a sealed primary circuit shall be fitted with an expansion vessel of sufficient capacity to accommodate, with the pressure differentials involved, the increase in volume of the water content of the whole of the primary system, including any space heating circuits, when heated from 10 °C to 110 °C. Indirect cylinders fitted in sealed primary circuits shall have primary heaters suitable for operating at a pressure of 0.35 bar in excess of the pressure relief valve setting. The specific requirements concerning the safety of sealed primary circuits given in **2.4** and **2.6** shall be conformed to in every case.

© BSI 1997

2.3.5.7 *Double feed and single feed primary circuits*

The primary circuit shall either be fed independently of the secondary system, e.g. double feed primary circuit, or be fed from the secondary system by using a hot water cylinder incorporating a special primary heat exchanger, i.e. single feed primary circuit. A single feed indirect cylinder shall only be used when both primary and secondary systems are of the vented type. Where a single feed indirect cylinder is used:

a) the cylinder shall conform to BS 1566 : Part 2 and shall be installed in accordance with the cylinder and appliance manufacturers' instructions;

b) where the primary circuit is pumped, the static head of the system shall be in excess of the maximum pump head;

c) no corrosion inhibitor or additive shall be introduced into the primary circuit;

d) the recommendations of the manufacturers of the boiler and the radiators as to the suitability of their products for use in this system shall be followed.

2.3.6 Supplementary water heating and independent summer water heating

Where supplementary electric heating is to be used in conjunction with a boiler, the height of the storage vessel above the boiler shall not be less than 1 m in order to prevent circulation of hot water from the storage vessel to the boiler.

COMMENTARY AND RECOMMENDATIONS ON 2.3.6

It is permissible for supplementary water heating and independent summer water heating to be provided in the storage vessel by an electric immersion heater, a gas-fired circulator, a heat pump or from solar energy.

Supplementary hot water may also be provided in the form of a single point gas or electric heater at the point of use.

2.3.7 Water heating by solar energy

Solar water heating shall be in accordance with BS 5918.

COMMENTARY AND RECOMMENDATIONS ON 2.3.7

Solar energy may be used to augment a conventional domestic water heating system of the boiler or immersion heater type, although in sunny weather solar energy alone may be sufficient.

2.3.8 Secondary distribution systems

In hot water systems incorporating a hot water storage vessel, the hot water supply or distributing pipe shall be arranged to be from the top of the vessel or as near thereto as practicable and always above any primary flow connection.

COMMENTARY AND RECOMMENDATIONS ON 2.3.8

Secondary water systems should be fed from a cold water storage cistern and fitted with an open vent pipe, or of unvented type supplied with cold water by gravity from a cold water storage cistern or from the mains supply to the building, either directly or through a pressure reducing valve.

To promote maximum economy of fuel and water the hot water distribution system should be designed so that hot water appears shortly after the taps are opened. To this end terminal branches should be as short as possible. The hot water pipe feeding a spray tap for hand washing should not exceed 1 m in length. When delivery points are situated at a distance from the water heater or hot water storage vessel, consideration should be given to the use of a separate water heater installed closer to those delivery points or insulating and electrically trace heating the flow pipework (see 2.7.4).

As an alternative a secondary circuit with flow and return pipes to the storage vessel could be considered but secondary circuits inevitably dissipate heat and should be avoided where possible. The return pipe should be connected to the hot water storage vessel at a point not lower than the level of the boiler flow pipe connection if there is one. (see 2.4).

2.3.9 System components

2.3.9.1 *Cold feed pipe*

The cold feed pipe to the hot water storage vessel or water heater shall be sized in accordance with 2.5. It shall discharge near the bottom of the heaters or storage vessels and if the system is cistern fed this pipe shall not supply any other fitting. A separate cold feed pipe from a separate expansion cistern shall be provided to the lowest point of a vented primary circuit in an indirect system unless a single feed hot water cylinder is used.

A servicing valve or stopvalve with a fixed washer plate shall be provided in a convenient and accessible position in every cold feed pipe other than those to a vented primary circuit which shall have a valve only when the capacity of the expansion cistern exceeds 18 l (see 2.3.5.6.1).

In direct type boiler systems the cold feed pipe and the return pipe to the boiler shall have their own connections to the hot water storage vessel.

2.3.9.2 *Open vent pipe*

The vent pipe to a storage type hot water system shall be taken from the top of the storage vessel or the highest point of the distribution pipework to a point above the cold feed cistern. An offset shall be included in the vent pipe close to its point of connection to the hot water storage vessel.

When a vented primary circuit is used in an indirect system, unless a single feed hot water storage cylinder is used, the vent pipe shall run from the highest point of the primary circuit to a point above the primary feed and expansion cistern at a height that will prevent a discharge of water from vent pipe and/or air entrainment into the system under normal working conditions. Due allowance shall be made for the head induced by any circulating pump used (see BS 5449 : Part 1).

For gravity circulation systems this height shall be not less than 150 mm plus 40 mm for every metre in the height of the overflow level above the lowest point of the cold feed pipe.

No valves shall be fitted to any vent pipe and the pipe shall rise continuously from its point of connection to the hot water system to its end except where it is permitted to be bent so as to terminate downwards (see figures 5 and 6). Vent pipes shall not be less than 19 mm bore.

One pipe shall not serve as both open vent pipe and cold feed pipe, unless the associated system or circuit has:

> 1) the energy supply to each heater under thermostatic control;
>
> 2) the energy supply to each heater fitted with a temperature-operated manually reset energy cut-out independent of the thermostatic control; and
>
> 3) a temperature relief valve in accordance with BS 6283 : Part 2, or a combined temperature and pressure relief valve in accordance with BS 6283 : Part 3, e.g. as required by BS 7206 and BS 3456 : Part 102 : Section 102.21 and BS EN 60335-2-21.

2.3.9.3 Hot water storage vessels

2.3.9.3.1 General

Storage vessels shall conform to BS 699, BS 853, BS 1566 : Parts 1 and 2, BS 3198 or BS 7206, as appropriate.

COMMENTARY AND RECOMMENDATIONS ON 2.3.9.3.1

It is recognized that special copper cylinders, that are not covered by British Standards, may be required where standard cylinders will not fit. The primary heaters in these cylinders should conform to BS 1566 : Part 1 (double feed) and Part 2 (single feed).

Apart from pressure considerations, the grade (wall thickness) of copper storage vessels, and also the need for protector rods, should be determined on the basis of the type of water supplied in the area. If necessary, the water supplier's advice should be sought.

2.3.9.3.2 Hot water storage capacities

The amount of hot water to be stored shall be related to the likely consumption and recovery rate.

COMMENTARY AND RECOMMENDATIONS ON 2.3.9.3.2

In dwellings the storage capacity should normally be based on 45 l per occupant unless pumped primary circuits or special appliances justify the use of smaller storage capacities.

A minimum hot water storage capacity of 100 l shall be used in solid fuel fired boiler hot water systems.

2.3.9.3.3 Insulation

The storage vessels shall be thermally insulated either by a jacket in accordance with BS 5615 or by factory applied thermal insulation in accordance with BS 699, BS 1566 or BS 3198, as appropriate, and in accordance with building regulations (see **A.1**). Where a segmented insulating jacket is used the segments of the jacket shall be taped together to provide a complete insulation cover for the storage vessel.

2.3.9.4 Cisterns and expansion vessels

Feed cisterns, expansion cisterns, combined feed and expansion cisterns and expansion vessels shall conform to BS 417, BS 4213, BS 4814 or BS 6144, as appropriate.

A cistern used only to feed the hot water supply system shall conform to all the requirements for a cold water storage cistern (see **2.2.3**). It shall have a capacity at least equal to that of the hot water cylinder. The feed cistern shall be situated at a height which will ensure a satisfactory flow of water at the highest point of discharge.

If there is a cold water storage cistern that supplies cold water to delivery points, and this is also used as the feed cistern for a direct system or for the secondary part only of an indirect system, it shall have a capacity of at least 230 l.

The feed and expansion cistern for the primary circuit of an indirect system shall be used only for that circuit and shall be able to accommodate the expansion of the water in the circuit if raised to boiling point. The increase in volume shall be taken as 4 % of the volume of the water in the circuit. The float-operated valve in an expansion cistern for a primary circuit shall incorporate adequate backflow protection (see **2.6.3.4.2**) or shall conform to BS 1212 : Part 2 or 3 and be installed at a level no lower than that of the warning pipe. The valve shall be adjusted to close when the water is cold at a level low enough to ensure that expansion on heating does not cause the water to rise higher than 25 mm below the over-flowing level of the warning pipe. The float shall be of a material suitable for use in hot water at a temperature of 100 °C.

No warning or overflow pipe from any cistern connected to a primary circuit shall be installed to convey water to any cistern from which water may be drawn for any domestic purpose.

COMMENTARY AND RECOMMENDATIONS ON 2.3.9.4

The use of float operated valves incorporating a drop lever is the preferred method of controlling a low level of water in the feed and expansion cistern to a primary circuit.

© BSI 1997

2.3.9.5 *Boilers*

2.3.9.5.1 *Appliances*

If the gas heater is not fitted with a CE mark, boilers and associated equipment shall conform to the following British Standards as applicable:

BS 1252

BS 1894

BS 3376

BS 3377

BS 3378

BS 4433

BS 4834

BS 4876

BS 5258 : Parts 1, 8 and 15

BS 5871 : Part 1

BS 6798

2.3.9.5.2 *Installation*

With boilers fired by solid fuel the manufacturer's recommendations shall be followed to ensure that all heat generated when the boiler is slumbering is dissipated. Neither this heat emitter nor its circuit shall be fitted with valves.

Boilers shall always be sited in a location in accordance with manufacturer's instructions. In the case of a non room-sealed appliance, provision for an adequate supply of air for combustion shall be made.

Provision shall be made for sufficient working space to enable maintenance to be carried out. There shall also be sufficient space and access to ensure that the boiler can be removed and replaced.

2.3.9.6 *Circulating pump*

Pumped circulation shall be provided in all cases where the natural circulating pressure available is insufficient to circulate the water around the system. (For examples of pumped systems, see annex C.)

Inlet and outlet connections to a circulating pump shall be fitted with fullway valves.

The circulating pump shall be installed in accordance with the manufacturer's recommendations and space shall be allowed for maintenance and removal.

Circulating pumps shall conform to BS 1394 : Part 2 and BS EN 60335-2-51.

2.3.9.7 *Valves and taps*

Valves used for isolating a section of the water service shall not leak when closed.

Sufficient draining taps conforming to BS 1010 or BS 2879 shall be fitted in accessible positions for draining the entire system.

Mixing valves (whether thermostatically controlled or not) and single outlet combination taps for mixing hot water and cold water and discharging the mixture shall be supplied with cold water from the same source, e.g. storage cistern or mains, that feeds the hot water system. Except for bath/shower single units, manually operated non-thermostatically controlled mixing valves shall not be used to control the water to more than one outlet.

COMMENTARY AND RECOMMENDATIONS ON 2.3.9.7

The requirement for mixing valves is especially important with showers and spray fittings.

The Health and Safety Executive guidance note HS(G) 104, 'Safe' hot water temperatures, refers to residential homes with reference to scalding protection [8].

2.3.9.8 *Safety devices*

Pressure relief valves, temperature relief valves and combined temperature and pressure relief valves, check valves, pressure reducing valves, anti-vacuum valves and pipe interrupters shall be fitted in accordance with **2.4** and **2.6** and shall conform to the relevant Part or Parts of BS 6280, BS 6281, BS 6282 and BS 6283.

2.3.10 Energy supply

Electric wiring shall be in accordance with BS 7671.

COMMENTARY AND RECOMMENDATIONS ON 2.3.10

Attention is drawn to the Gas Safety (Installation and Use) Regulations for all gas installation work (see A.4).

When a gas-fired instantaneous water heater is used in rooms other than bathrooms, the room-sealed type should be selected whenever possible. Instantaneous water heaters have relatively high power ratings and the need to provide an adequate electricity or gas supply should be taken into account. The rate of flow of hot water, the temperature rise from feed to delivery, the power consumption and the efficiency of the appliance are related by the formula:

$$FT = 14.3EP$$

where

F is the flow rate (in l/min);

T is the temperature rise (in K);

E is the efficiency (ratio of power output to power input);

P is the power input rating (in kW).

If the appliance efficiency is not known, a value of 0.75 may be assumed for gas-fired instantaneous water heaters and 0.90 for electric instantaneous water heaters. This will give a conservative estimate of the flow available for a given temperature rise. Single outlet instantaneous water heaters may be inlet controlled or outlet controlled. Multi-outlet heaters are outlet controlled only and are most satisfactory when only one outlet is used at any one time. For economy in use of fuel and water the heater should be located as close as possible to the hot water outlet in most frequent use, usually the kitchen tap. When close control of temperature is required, e.g. for a shower, thermostatic safety control and/or the use of a heater fitted with a water governor is recommended. Alternatively, the heater should be fed from a storage cistern through its own separate feed pipe; most instantaneous shower units require a minimum supply pressure of about 1 bar[1] or 10 m head. For information on shower installations, reference should be made to BS 6340 : Part 4.

2.4 Prevention of bursting

Water heaters shall have temperature control and safety devices that ensure that the water temperature does not exceed 100 °C and all fittings and pipework used in the water system shall be protected from bursting.

2.4.1 Water heaters

Electric instantaneous water heaters shall conform to BS EN 60335-2-35 and electric storage heaters shall conform to BS EN 60335-2-21.

COMMENTARY AND RECOMMENDATIONS ON 2.4.1

The production of steam in a closed vessel, or the heating of water under pressure to a temperature in excess of 100 °C can be extremely dangerous. A proportion of the water heated in this way flashes into steam when it escapes to atmospheric pressure, with a correspondingly large increase in volume. If such steam escapes in an uncontrolled way, as would result from the rupture of the containing vessel, an explosion will occur. This standard deals only with low temperature systems; consequently a key requirement is that the highest water temperature does not exceed 100 °C at any time at any point in the system. This standard does not deal with systems that are designed to operate with steam or high temperature hot water.

Successful and continuing safe operation of a system is, in practice, dependent upon having the right equipment correctly installed in a well designed system that is properly maintained and not exposed to misguided interference.

The use of appliances that have all the necessary safety devices already fitted to them at the factory is recommended to ensure correct assembly and calibration.

The reliability and durability of the equipment on which the safety of the installation depends should be considered, bearing in mind the conditions under which it will operate.

On installation, the user should be made aware of the need for regular maintenance.

Equipment susceptible to interference should be protected against this risk. The selection of all equipment, its location and even the choice of system will be influenced by these factors.

---

[1] 1 bar = 10^5 N/m^2 = 10^5 Pa

© BSI 1997

2.4.2 Energy controls and safety devices

2.4.2.1 Except for systems where water is heated by a source that itself is incapable of raising the temperature above 90 °C, or for instantaneous electric water heaters with a capacity of 15 l or less that are fitted with a CE mark, or for instantaneous gas water heaters with a capacity of 15 l or less that are fitted with a CE mark or conform to BS 5386 : Part 1, 2 or 5 as appropriate, wherever stored water is heated, the following conditions apply.

a) Vented systems:

1) except where water in a vented system is heated by a boiler fired by solid fuel as specified in 5.1 b) of BS 5449 : 1990, the energy supply to each heater or store shall be under thermostatic control;

2) a means of dissipating the power input under temperature fault conditions shall be provided in the form of an adequate vent to atmosphere;

3)

i) in a gas fuelled system, the energy supply to each heater shall be fitted with a temperature operated, manually reset energy cut-out independent of the thermostatic control in those cases where it is a requirement of BS EN 297 or BS EN 625, as appropriate;

ii) in the case of a vented primary or secondary circuit where any materials in contact with the water, including existing feed cistern(s) and cover(s), are not capable of withstanding a temperature of 100 °C without detrimental effect, the energy supply to each heater shall be fitted with a temperature operated, manually reset energy cut-out independent of the thermostatic control and set to operate before a temperature of 100 °C can be reached.

b) Unvented systems containing 15 l or less storage capacity:

1) the energy supply to each heater shall be under thermostatic control;

2) the energy supply to each heater shall be fitted with a temperature operated manually reset energy cut-out independent of the thermostatic control; and

3)

i) in those cases where it is a requirement of BS EN 60335-2-21, electric storage water heaters shall be fitted with a means of dissipating the power input in the form of a temperature relief valve to BS 6283 : Part 2 or a combined temperature and pressure relief valve to BS 6283 : Part 3;

ii) in the case of a boiler conforming to BS 5258 : Part 1, Part 8 or Part 15, or fitted with a CE mark, as appropriate, the system shall be fitted with a means of preventing excess pressure under fault conditions, in the form of a pressure relief valve.

c) Unvented systems greater than 15 l storage capacity of stored domestic water

All controls and safety devices shall be factory fitted by the manufacturer. Thermostats, temperature operated energy cut-outs and temperature relief valves or combined temperature and pressure relief valves shall be set so that they operate in that sequence as temperature rises. In addition:

1) the energy supply to each heater shall be under thermostatic control;

2) the energy supply to each heater shall be fitted with a temperature operated manually reset energy cut-out independent of the thermostatic control; and

3) a temperature relief valve in accordance with BS 6283 : Part 2 shall be fitted, or a combined temperature and pressure relief valve in accordance with BS 6283 : Part 3, e.g. as required by BS 7206 and BS 3456 : Part 102 : Section 102.21 and BS EN 60335-2-21.

d) Unvented water jacketed tube heaters greater than 15 l storage capacity:

1) the energy supply to each heater shall be under thermostatic control;

2) the energy supply to each heater shall be fitted with a temperature-operated non self-resetting thermal cut-out independent of the thermostatic; and

3) a means of dissipating the power input under temperature fault conditions shall be provided in the form of a temperature relief valve in accordance with BS 6283 : Part 2, or a combined temperature and pressure relief valve in accordance with BS 6283 : Part 3, or a second temperature-operated non self-resetting cut-out with diversity of operation and different from the thermostat and temperature-operated non self-resetting thermal energy cut-out in 2).

COMMENTARY AND RECOMMENDATIONS ON 2.4.2.1 a) 3) ii)

BS 5449 and, where applicable, BS 5546 both require feed cisterns in new or replacement installations to withstand a temperature of 100 °C. See both of these standards for further details.

2.4.2.2 Where their performance is not defined in the relevant appliance standard, thermostats and temperature operated manually reset energy cut-outs shall conform to BS 3955 or BS EN 257, as appropriate; electromechanical (motorized) valves forming part of a temperature operated manually reset energy cut-out shall conform to BS 3955, where applicable; combined temperature and pressure relief valves shall conform to BS 6283 : Part 3 : 1991 and temperature relief valves shall conform to BS 6283 : Part 2 : 1991.

2.4.2.3 Any vent pipework shall be of such a size that it is capable of carrying away the maximum power input from the heater into the water at the normal working pressure of the system. The minimum internal diameter of a vent pipe shall be 19 mm. There shall be an unimpeded route for the hot discharge from the heater and an unimpeded route for the cold make-up water to reach the heater. There shall be no valve between the heater and the discharge point of the vent. A full way stop valve of a type that cannot act as a check valve shall be installed in the outlet from the feed cistern.

2.4.2.4 Any temperature relief valve or combined temperature and pressure relief valve shall be located directly on the storage vessel that it is intended to protect, so as to sense the water temperature within the vessel. No valves shall be fitted between the temperature relief valve or combined temperature and pressure relief valve and the vessel.

A temperature relief valve or combined temperature and pressure relief valve shall:

a) be located directly on the storage vessel, such that the temperature of the stored water does not exceed 100 °C; and

b) only discharge water at below its operating temperature when subjected to a pressure at least 0.5 bar greater than the maximum working pressure in the vessel to which they are fitted.

In the case of units or assembled packages provided with a direct means of heating, the temperature relief valve or combined temperature and pressure relief valve shall have a discharge rating at least equal to the maximum power input to the water.

In the case of units provided only with a primary heater (i.e. indirectly heated), the temperature relief valve or combined temperature and pressure relief valve, when tested in accordance with the water discharge test of BS 6283 : Part 2 or 3, as appropriate, shall discharge water at a rate not less than 500 kg/h.

The temperature relief valve or combined temperature and pressure relief valve discharge pipe shall be at least the same size as the outlet of the valve.

The discharge shall be through an air break over a tundish located in the same room or internal space and vertically as near as is possible and in any case within 500 mm of the temperature relief valve or combined temperature and pressure relief valve. The discharge pipe from the tundish outlet shall extend downwards in a vertical direction for not less than 300 mm below the outlet before any bends are permitted in the pipe. The discharge pipe shall be laid to a gradient for drainage, and shall be of a suitable metal such as copper or stainless steel. The size of the tundish discharge pipe shall be at least one size larger than the nominal outlet size of the valve, unless its total equivalent hydraulic resistance exceeds that of a straight pipe 9 m long, i.e. discharge pipes between 9 m and 18 m equivalent resistance length shall be at least two sizes larger than the nominal outlet size of the valve, between 18 m and 27 m at least three sizes larger, and so on; see figure D.2 and table D.3 of annex D for further details of equivalent pipe lengths.

2.4.2.5 If a non-mechanical safety device, such as a fusible plug, is fitted to any hot water storage vessel, that vessel shall also be fitted with a temperature relief valve or combined temperature and pressure relief valve designed to operate at a temperature not less than 5 °C below that at which the non-mechanical device operates or is designed to operate.

2.4.2.6 Where unvented hot water heaters incorporate an internal or external expansion facility an expansion valve, conforming to BS 6283 : Part 1, shall be installed in the cold feed pipework to the heater or hot water cylinder and no valve shall separate it from the heater or hot water cylinder. This does not preclude the provision of a draining tap at any position on the pipework.

2.4.2.7 In the case of a vented system, the vent pipe for the circuit shall be protected from freezing and where appropriate (see 2.3.9.2), shall terminate over the feed cistern supplying that circuit and rise to a height above the cistern sufficient to prevent a discharge except under fault conditions.

2.4.2.8 In the case of an unvented system, the discharge from any temperature relief valve or combined temperature and pressure relief valve or any expansion relief valve shall be located so that it is safe (i.e. it cannot create a hazard to persons in or around the building or cause damage to electrical components and wiring), and provides a visible warning of fault conditions.

COMMENTARY AND RECOMMENDATIONS ON 2.4.2

Temperature relief valves or combined temperature and pressure relief valves, expansion valves, temperature operated non-self-resetting thermal cut-outs and thermostats should be accessible, and all controls/devices should be located to avoid uninformed interference.

In the event of failure of the electrical safety devices fitted to an unvented system, the temperature relief valve will discharge all the hot water within the cylinder at a flow rate of typically of 12 l/min to 20 l/min. The water will be at a temperature approaching boiling point.

The statutory requirements for unvented hot water storage systems are given in the following:

– England and Wales: The Building Regulations 1991 : Part G3.

– Scotland: The Building (Standards) Regulations 1990: Part II, clauses 27 and 28.

– Northern Ireland: The Building Regulations (Northern Ireland) 1990 : Part 5.

The above regulations do not apply to:

a) a hot water storage system that has storage vessel with a capacity of 15l or less;

b) a system providing space heating only;

c) a system which heats or stores water for the purposes only of an industrial process.

© BSI 1997

Where there is the possibility of a water to steam explosion, engineering or reliability studies recommend the use of more than one safety device. If replenishment water is supplied, for example, to a conventional storage water heater then the commonly used safety devices are a temperature operated non self-resetting thermal cut-out and a combined temperature and pressure relief valve. These safety devices have different modes of operation and act upon different aspects of the system, i.e. the temperature operated non self-resetting thermal cut-out operates upon the source of power, and the combined temperature and pressure relief valve dissipates power by discharging hot water. However, when there is no replenishment water, as with some water jacketed tube heaters, a combined temperature and pressure relief valve may not be suitable. To protect this type of appliance a second temperature operated non self-resetting thermal cut-out with diversity of operation and different from the thermostat and first temperature operated non self-resetting thermal cut-out may be used, e.g. operating on a circulating pump if that pump delivers heated water to the store.

An unvented system without third party approval is unlikely to be accepted by local authorities where the system comes under building regulation control.

2.4.3 Pressure control

Whether hot or cold water is involved, no part of the system shall burst due to the hydraulic pressures to which it is subjected. The pressures in the system shall never exceed the safe working pressures of the component parts.

Where necessary the supply pressure shall be controlled by using break cisterns or pressure reducing valves in accordance with BS 6283 : Part 4. If the supply to a storage type water heater is through a pressure reducing valve of the type that permits backflow, the working pressure in the system shall be assumed to be the maximum pressure upstream of the valve.

The expansion or combined temperature and pressure relief valve settings shall be the maximum working pressure plus 0.5 bar to 1.5 bar.

For unvented systems provision shall be made to accommodate expansion by either:

a) allowing expansion water to travel back along the feed pipe, provided that heated water cannot reach any communication pipe or branch feeding a cold water outlet. Where such reverse flow is impeded by a stopvalve with a loose washer plate, this valve shall be replaced by a valve with a fixed washer plate;

b) providing an expansion vessel, in accordance with BS 6144, or an integral air space, to accommodate expansion water where reverse flow along the cold feed is prevented, for example, by a check valve, some types of pressure reducing valve or a stopvalve with a loose washer plate. This expansion vessel or integral air space shall be sized in accordance with the volume of water heated so the pressure is limited to the maximum working pressure for the system.

2.4.4 Maintenance of water level

Primary flow and return pipes shall not be connected to delivery pipes, and any drain taps fitted shall have removable keys.

An adequate means to supply make-up water shall be fitted in an independent primary circuit. Where there is no permanent connection to the water supply system, a notice drawing attention to the required frequency of inspection shall be displayed in a prominent place. This type of system shall not be used when the energy input is not under complete thermostatic control.

Where the energy input to the primary circuit of a direct or an indirect system is not under complete thermostatic control, for example, with types of solid fuel heating, the secondary pipework shall be arranged so that the taps cannot reduce the level of the water level in the cylinder or tank below the level of the primary flow connection when the secondary cold feed is interrupted or restricted.

COMMENTARY AND RECOMMENDATIONS ON 2.4.4

The unintentional draining of a system is dangerous and is to be avoided, as it may expose temperature controls thus impairing their operation, or it may expose the heating surfaces of the heater, which then becomes overheated. Where these are situated in the upper part of a system they are correspondingly more vulnerable to a fall in water level. When they are situated below the level of the return pipe connection to the tank or cylinder, absence of hot water at the delivery points should give some advance warning of the fall in water level.

As a consequence it is recommended that the hot water delivery connection is located at the top of the hot water cylinder in conjunction with a suitably located vent, or, in the case of some unvented systems, an anti vacuum valve. Where hot water is delivered through a secondary circulating system, the recommendations given in 2.3.8 should be followed.

2.5 Pipe sizing

The system shall be designed and installed so that the design flow rates given in table 3 shall be available at each outlet and any group of outlets where the total demand does not exceed 0.3 l/s, when only that outlet or group of outlets are open. When simultaneous discharge occurs the rate of flow of water at any outlet in use shall be not less than the minimum rate given in table 3.

The pipes and fittings shall be sized so that the maximum velocity does not exceed 3.0 m/s. This maximum shall not apply to small bore connections of limited length supplied as parts of combination tap assemblies.

The design flow rates to storage cisterns shall be determined by dividing the cistern's capacity by the required filling time. Where single dwellings are supplied from individual minimal sized storage cisterns, filling time shall be less than 1 h.

COMMENTARY AND RECOMMENDATIONS ON 2.5

Simultaneous use of appliances may reduce flow rates, possibly below design values. It is important therefore that the whole system should be designed so that flow rates are not reduced to such an extent as to adversely affect the satisfactory functioning of the system. In particular, where the reduction in flow could affect the temperature of water delivered to showers, measures should be taken to protect the user against excessive water temperatures (see 2.3.2).

In most buildings appliances are rarely in simultaneous use, therefore for reasons of economy, it is usual to provide for a demand less than the total demand of all appliances being in use at the same time.

The simultaneous demand can be determined from data derived by observation and experience of similar installations, or by the application of probability theory. A system of determination based on probability theory using loading units, which take into consideration the flow rate required at the appliance, the length of time in use, and the frequency of use is described in annex D.

Filling times for cisterns could be 4 h, depending on the amount of storage provided, the rate of flow of water available from the source or main and whether the supply is constant.

In other than small, simple installations, such as single dwellings, pipe sizes should be calculated using a recognized method of calculation, such as the method given in annex D.

Table 3. Design flow rates

Outlet fitting or appliance	Rate of flow l/s	
	Design rate	Min. rate
WC cistern (to fill in 2 min)	0.13	0.10
WC flushing trough (per WC served) (see Note 2)	0.15	0.10
Urinal cistern (each position served)	0.004	0.002
Washbasin	0.15	0.10
Handbasin (pillar taps)	0.15	0.10
Handbasin (spray or spray mixer taps)	0.05	0.03
Bidet	0.20	0.10
Bath (G $\frac{3}{4}$)	0.30	0.20
Bath (G 1)	0.60	0.40
Shower head (see Note 4)	0.20	0.10
Kitchen sink (G $\frac{1}{2}$)	0.20	0.10
Kitchen sink (G $\frac{3}{4}$)	0.30	0.20
Kitchen sink (G 1)	0.60	0.40
Washing machine	0.20	0.15
Dish-washing machine (see Note 1)	0.15	0.10

NOTE 1. The manufacturer should be consulted for required flow rates to washing and dish-washing machines for other than single dwellings.

NOTE 2. WC flushing troughs are recommended where anticipated use of WCs is more frequent than once per minute.

NOTE 3. Mixer fittings or combination tap assemblies deliver less flow than two separate taps; it is suggested that 70 % of the above flow rates may be sufficient.

NOTE 4. The rate of flow required to shower heads will depend on the type fitted and the advice of the shower manufacturer should be sought.

© BSI 1997

2.6 Preservation of water quality

2.6.1 General

2.6.1.1 The installation shall be constructed so that water delivered is not liable to become contaminated or that contamination of the undertaker's supply does not occur.

COMMENTARY AND RECOMMENDATIONS ON 2.6.1.1

Water suppliers are obliged to provide a supply of water which is suitable and safe for drinking

2.6.1.2 The installation shall not adversely affect drinking water:

a) by materials in contact with the water being unsuitable for the purpose;

b) as a result of backflow of water from water fittings, or water using appliances, into pipework connected to mains or to other fittings and appliances;

c) by cross-connection between pipes conveying water supplied by the water undertaker with pipes conveying water from some other source;

d) by stagnation, particularly at high temperatures.

2.6.1.3 No pump or similar apparatus, the purpose of which is to increase the pressure in or rate of flow from a supply pipe or any fitting or appliance connected to a supply pipe, shall be connected unless the prior written permission of the water supplier has been obtained in each instance.

COMMENTARY AND RECOMMENDATIONS ON 2.6.1.3

The use of such a pump or similar apparatus is likely to lead to pressure reduction in the upstream pipework which, if significant, increases the risk of backflow from other fittings.

2.6.2 Prevention of contact of water with unsuitable materials of construction

2.6.2.1 In order to ensure that any materials or products used in the manufacture, installation or repair of water fittings and appliances likely to be in contact with water will not have an adverse effect on water quality, materials shall be in accordance with BS 6920 or BS 7766, as appropriate.

No pipe, fitting or storage cistern shall be lined or coated internally with coal tar or any material that includes coal tar.

No copper pipe shall be connected to any lead pipe or lead-lined cistern, even by way of repair or replacement, unless corrosion of the lead by galvanic action is prevented.

2.6.2.2 No pipe or fitting shall be laid in, on, or through foul soil, refuse, an ashpit, sewer, drain, cesspool or refuse chute, or any manhole connected with them.

No pipe susceptible to deterioration by contact with any substance shall be laid or installed in a place where such deterioration is likely to occur.

No pipe that is permeable to any contaminant shall be laid or installed in any position where permeation is likely to occur.

COMMENTARY AND RECOMMENDATIONS ON 2.6.2.2

Copper tube with a factory applied protective plastics coating should be considered where ground contamination occurs.

2.6.2.3 If a liquid (other than water) is used in any type of heating primary circuit which transfers heat to water for domestic use, or if an additive is used in water in such a circuit, the liquid or additive shall be non-toxic and non-corrosive.

2.6.3 Prevention of contamination of water as a consequence of backflow

2.6.3.1 *General*

Measures shall be taken to prevent:

a) the ingress of contamination to any part of a water installation; and

b) the backflow of water from the installation to the supply mains.

A backflow prevention device shall be arranged or connected at or as near as practicable to each point of delivery and use of water in accordance with table 4 and the other requirements of this clause. Appliances with built-in backflow prevention shall be capable of passing the test described in BS 6280.

All backflow prevention devices shall be installed so that they are accessible for examination, repair or replacement.

In addition to the methods of prevention given in table 4, secondary backflow prevention shall be provided on every supply or distribution pipe that serves two or more separately occupied premises and on every supply pipe that conveys water to premises that are required to provide a storage cistern capable of holding sufficient water for at least 24 h normal use.

COMMENTARY AND RECOMMENDATIONS ON 2.6.3.1

Table 4 covers many commonly occurring situations and gives the appropriate backflow prevention device in each case. It takes into account the particular risk and its potential effect on health, the likely frequency of the presence of that risk and the reliability of the backflow prevention device. Backflow prevention devices are listed in grade order with the highest first. The table lists the lowest acceptable grade of backflow prevention device for each risk but a higher grade of device may be used in place of that given if desired; in many instances a higher grade will be more convenient. The appropriate protection for situations not listed in table 4 is that for listed situations having an equivalent or greater level of risk than the unlisted situation.

Table 4. Backflow prevention measures to be used with various types of water fittings and appliances

Backflow prevention device	Water fitting or appliances
Type A air gap as specified in **2.6.3.4.1** or an interposed cistern as specified in **2.6.3.4.2**	Any point of use where a substance harmful to health is continuously or frequently present, e.g.: WC pan; urinal bowl; bidet; bedpan washer; dental sputum bowl; water treatment plant other than water softening plant; fire sprinkler systems containing anti-freeze; any appliance or cistern that can receive water not supplied by a water supplier; permanently connected sealed central heating; system other than in a dwelling; hose union tap not on domestic premises[1]; poultry and animal drinking troughs; installations in laboratories, dairies, slaughter house, butchery and meat trade premises; dye works and sewage works; bottle washing apparatus; industrial chemical baths; cisterns connected to central heating systems other than in dwellings; agricultural storage cisterns.
Type B air gap as specified in **2.6.3.4.3**, or pipe interrupter as specified in **2.6.3.4.4**, or double check valve assembly as specified in **2.6.3.4.8** or combined check valve and anti-vacuum valve as specified in **2.6.3.4.7**	Any point of use or draw-off where a substance harmful to health may be present, e.g.: vented primary hot water circuits and associated cisterns in dwellings; dialysis machine with integral membrane washing facility; hose union tap on domestic premises (e.g. in a kitchen, garage or garden); shower hose where shower head could be submerged in any sanitary appliance common-salt regenerated water softening plant in any premises other than a single dwelling; permanent standpipe supplying water to boats in marinas; temporary standpipe on mains, supplying water to mobile apparatus or construction sites; temporary connection to supply pipe of sealed primary circuits in single dwellings; clothes washing machine, dishwasher or tumble drier connected permanently or temporarily to a water service. Only a type B air gap or a pipe interrupter is acceptable and the protection shall be incorporated in the appliance. Machines that conform to BS 6614 have acceptable protection incorporated. If installed in premises other than a single dwelling the water supply to the machine or machines shall be from a cistern as specified in **2.6.3.4.2** and that cistern shall supply water only to machines with built-in backflow protection. Drink vending or dispensing machine in which any ingredient or gas is injected under pressure WC flushing cistern not supplied through a float-operated valve conforming to BS 1212 : Part 2 or 3 installed with the centre line of the valve body no lower than the highest water level under overflowing conditions.

© BSI 1997

Table 4. Backflow prevention measures to be used with various types of water fittings and appliances (*continued*)

Backflow prevention device	Water fitting or appliances
Check valve as specified in 2.6.3.4.6.	Any point of delivery or use where a substance harmful to health is not or is unlikely to be present, e.g.:
	common-salt regenerated water softener in single dwelling;
	home dialysing machine without integral membrane washing facility;
	fire sprinkler system without storage connected to a supply pipe;
	drink vending or dispensing machine in which no ingredient or gas is injected under pressure.

[1] Unless the fitting incorporates, as close as practicable to the point of use, a double check valve assembly or a combined check valve and anti-vacuum valve, and the fitting has been installed with written permission from the water supplier.

NOTE. A WC cistern supplied with water through a float-operated valve conforming to BS 1212 : Part 2 or 3 installed with the centre line of the valve body no lower than the highest water level under overflowing conditions normally requires no additional back-siphonage protection.

2.6.4 Prevention of contamination of drinking water by legionella

Measures shall be taken in the design and installation of cold and hot water systems to prevent the colonization of the system with legionella. These shall include the avoidance of:

a) stagnation of water in pipes, cisterns and other storage vessels;

b) water temperatures dwelling in the range of 20 °C to 45 °C;

c) use of materials that can harbour or provide nutrient for bacteria and other organisms;

d) installation of fittings where there is a potential for aerosol formation.

COMMENTARY AND RECOMMENDATIONS ON 2.6.4

Good practice is assumed if the recommendations contained in the Approved Code of Practice L8(rev) [3], and the Health and Safety Executive's booklet HS(G)70 [4] together with the other guidance documents [2,5,6] listed in the list of references, are followed.

The code of practice draws particular attention to:

a) hot water services where the volume of hot water in the system exceeds 300 l; and

b) cold and hot water services irrespective of size in premises where occupants are particularly susceptible, such as health care premises.

In order to reduce the risk of colonization of a water system the temperature of cold water in pipes and cisterns should not exceed 20 °C, and hot water should be stored and distributed at a temperature of not less than 60 °C with a temperature at the discharge point of 50 °C after 1 min.

Cold and hot water pipework should be as short as practicable, especially where it only serves infrequently used taps and fittings.

2.7 Maintenance of water temperature within the system

2.7.1 General

Installations shall be protected against conditions arising from adverse temperatures external to pipes, fittings and appliances. Protection shall be provided against:

a) ice formation in pipework and fittings;

b) heating of cold supply pipes;

c) condensation.

Where the placing of pipes and fittings above ground outside buildings is unavoidable, these pipes and fittings shall be protected by insulation with a weatherproof finish, in accordance with **2.7.3**. Where pipes rise from the ground, the insulation shall extend to the depth below ground stated in **2.7.3**.

COMMENTARY AND RECOMMENDATIONS ON 2.7.1

Suitable precautions or protection methods which need to be taken to reduce the risk of bursting, interruption of supply, waste, leakage and consequent damage to the building are the provision of:

a) insulation;

b) trace heating tapes; or

c) local heating.

In winter, water may only just be above freezing point when delivered into the consumer's pipes and a further reduction in temperature could cause freezing. Particularly vulnerable locations which require protection include those where flow is very slow, infrequent or through small diameter pipes.

To prevent freezing of water services in buildings it is preferable to keep the inside of the building continuously warm by the provision and maintenance of adequate heating. When the whole building is not heated, or where heating is only intermittent, heating of water pipes and fittings (trace heating) or heating their immediate surroundings (local heating) may suffice.

The layout of the water service should be planned to avoid the following:

a) external locations above ground;

b) unheated spaces;

c) positions near a window, air brick or other ventilator, external door or any other place where cold draughts are likely to occur;

d) a chase or duct formed in an external wall.

Care should be taken in the control of temperatures where trace heating is installed with plastics pipes.

2.7.2 Protection of water pipes and fittings

2.7.2.1 *Underground pipes*

Pipes laid underground outside buildings and not insulated in accordance with **2.7.3** shall be laid at a depth sufficient to give protection against freezing and no less than 0.75 m (see figure 11 and **2.1.8**).

COMMENTARY AND RECOMMENDATIONS ON 2.7.2.1

Underground stopvalves should not be brought up to a higher level merely for ease of access.

2.7.2.2 *Pipes entering buildings*

Where pipes rise from below the ground, the insulation shall extend to at least 0.75 m below the ground, in accordance with 2.7.3. (See figure 11, 3.1.6.2 and 2.8.2).

© BSI 1997

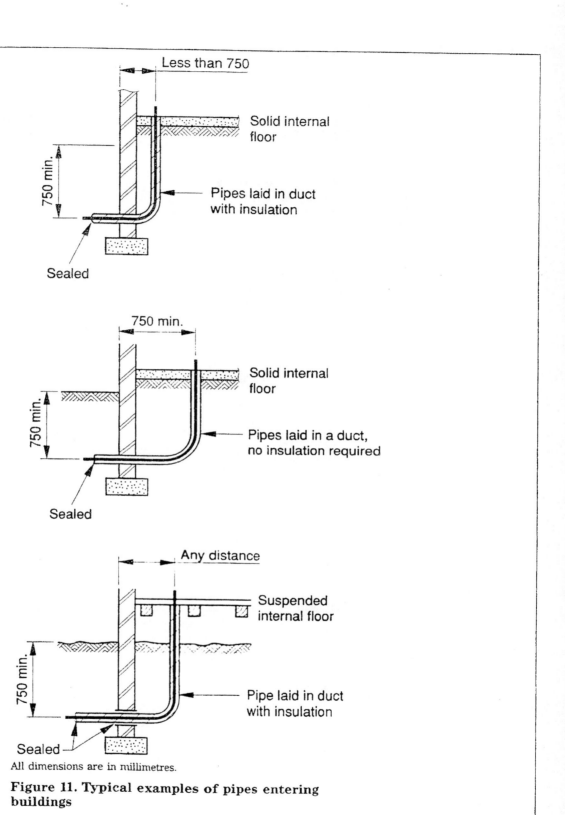

All dimensions are in millimetres.

Figure 11. Typical examples of pipes entering buildings

2.7.2.3 Pipes and fittings inside buildings

Pipes and fittings shall be insulated in accordance with **2.7.3**.

Insulation shall be provided on the top and sides of any cistern.

COMMENTARY AND RECOMMENDATIONS ON 2.7.2.3

Where pipes are attached to the inside faces of external walls in a part of a building that is heated, it should not be necessary to insulate them, but it is advantageous to fix such pipes clear of the wall on brackets or clipped to a pipe board.

Cold water pipes should be protected to prevent the formation of condensation. Where cold water pipes pass through areas of relatively high humidity, condensation will form unless prevented. Insulation, as a measure of prevention of condensation, is subject to the same requirements as insulation against heat loss or gain (see 2.7.3).

2.7.3 Insulation

Thermal insulating materials shall conform to BS 5422 and shall be installed in accordance with BS 5970.

The minimum thickness of thermal insulating materials used for the protection of water pipes and fittings shall be as given in tables 6 and 7.

Where cold water pipes pass through areas of relatively high dew point, they shall be insulated to prevent condensation.

Table 6. Calculated minimum thickness of insulation to protect copper pipes fixed inside premises for domestic cold water systems.

Outside diameter	Inside diameter (bore)	Thermal conductivity at 0 °C W/(m·K)			
		0.025	0.035	0.045	0.055
		Thickness of insulation			
mm	mm	mm			
15	13.6	30	62	124	241
22	20.2	12	20	30	43
28	26.2	8	12	17	23
35	32.6	6	9	12	15
42	39.6	5	7	9	11

Table 7. Calculated minimum thickness of insulation to protect copper pipes fixed inside premises against freezing for commercial and institutional applications[1]

Outside diameter	Inside diameter (bore)	Thermal conductivity W/(m·K)			
		0.025	0.035	0.045	0.055
		Thickness of insulation			
mm	mm	mm			
15.0	13.6	31	56	83	109
22.0	20.2	13	21	31	45
28.0	26.2	8	13	18	24
35.0	32.6	7	9	13	16
42.0	39.6	5	7	9	12
54.0	51.6	4	5	7	8
76.1	73.1	3	4	5	6
108.0	105.0	2	3	3	4
Above 108.0 mm outside diameter and flat surfaces		2	3	3	4

[1]Water temperature, +5 °C; ambient temperature, −3 °C; evaluation period, 24 h; permitted ice formation 50 %.

© BSI 1997

COMMENTARY AND RECOMMENDATIONS ON 2.7.3

Insulation slows down but does not prevent loss of heat from the water. Insulation will not give complete protection if the temperature falls to or below freezing point. However, a suitable thickness of insulation will delay the onset of freezing.

The thickness of insulating materials specified in BS 5422, whilst giving protection, is not considered practicable for protection of small diameter pipes fixed inside buildings. However, the thickness of insulating material identified in table 6, under the appropriate thermal conductivity values, is considered practicable and suitable for small diameter pipework and will provide reasonable protection for pipes fixed inside normally occupied buildings.

Unless the insulation material used is itself sufficiently impermeable to water vapour, a vapour barrier with a permeance not exceeding 0.05 g/(s MN) should be applied on the outside surface of the insulation and protected against damage if necessary.

Table 8. Examples of insulating materials

Thermal conductivity W/(m·K)	Material
Less than 0.020	Rigid phenolic foam
0.021 to 0.035	Polyurethane foam
0.040 to 0.055	Corkboard
0.055 to 0.07	Exfoliated vermiculite (loose fill)

2.7.4 Local and trace heating

Electric trace heating shall conform to BS 6351 : Part 1.

Any trace heating provided for the protection of any pipes or fittings shall be additional to, and not in substitution for insulation referred to in **2.7**.

COMMENTARY AND RECOMMENDATIONS ON 2.7.4

Local heating, in conjunction with a frost-thermostat, should only be used where other methods of frost protection are unsuitable, e.g. for pipes in unheated roof spaces when it is inconvenient to drain them and the building is to be unheated for a period during the winter.

Where trace heating is provided, it should be fitted before the insulation is applied.

2.7.5 Drainage of system to prevent frost damage

Arrangements shall be provided for isolating and draining pipes and fittings (see **2.2.5** to **2.2.7**).

Where a building is divided into parts the pipes and fittings in each part shall be arranged so that they may be isolated and drained without affecting the supply to any other part. Stopvalves shall be located in positions convenient for use as close as practicable to the point of entry of the pipe into the building or part thereof. Unless the stopvalve is installed within a normally heated building it shall be protected against freezing in accordance with **2.7.1** to **2.7.4**.

Every external standpipe, livestock watering appliance, garden tap, garage tap, or similar water fitting shall be supplied through a stopvalve which is located in a position convenient for use within a normally heated building or is protected against freezing in accordance with **2.7**.

The pipes and fittings in any part of a building not used in winter, any unheated building or part of a building, including any water-closet, garage or conservatory, or any other outbuilding, shall be arranged so as to enable them to be isolated and drained separately.

2.8 Accessibility of pipes and water fittings

2.8.1 General

The design of a system shall allow ready access to pipes and fittings for the purposes of inspection, maintenance and replacement (see figure 12).

COMMENTARY AND RECOMMENDATIONS ON 2.8.1

Other factors that may be considered are:

a) The use to which the building is to be put: importance of aesthetic considerations; consequences of leakage from inaccessible parts of the pipework; whether or not the system will be subject to routine inspection and maintenance.

b) The increase or decrease in capital or maintenance costs arising from the provision of improved accessibility: ease of forming ducts or chases; changes to pipe runs; ease of provision of removable access panels or covers; availability of multi-service walkways or crawlways in which water pipes may be installed.

c) The pipework materials and jointing methods: reliability of joints; resistance to both internal and external corrosion; flexibility of pipe when inserted in curved ducts or sleeves.

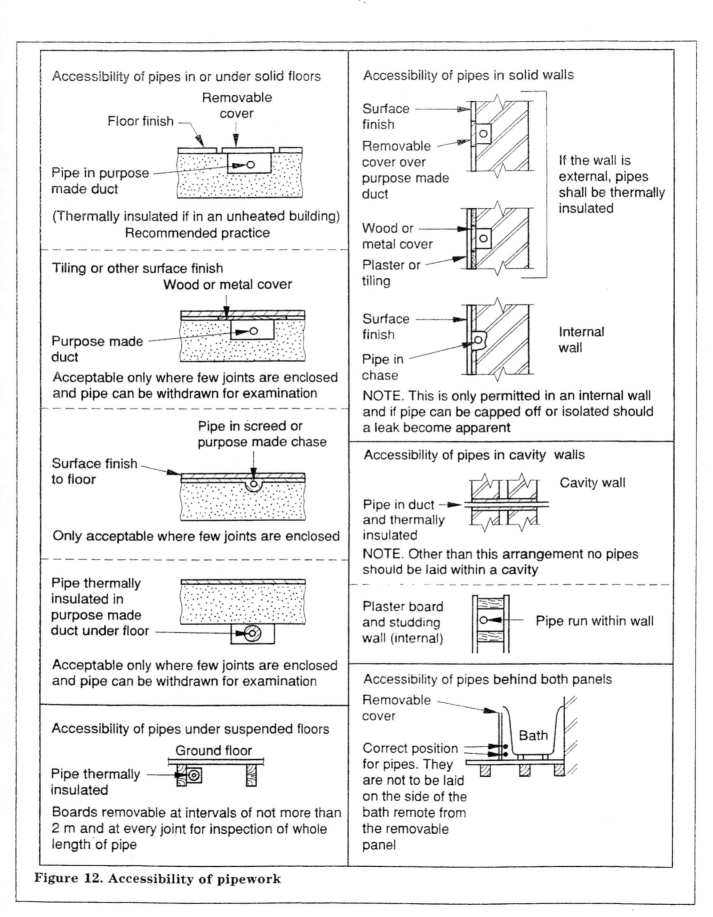

Figure 12. Accessibility of pipework

© BSI 1997

2.8.2 Pipes passing through walls and floors

2.8.2.1 No pipe shall be installed in the cavity of an external cavity wall. Where a pipe passes through any wall or floor, there shall be adequate provision for movement of the pipe relative to the wall or floor, by the use of a sleeve properly bonded into the wall or floor or by other no less suitable means. (See also **3.1.6.2**.)

2.8.2.2 Where fire regulations and other considerations require the ends of sleeves to be sealed, such sealing shall be of a permanently flexible form to allow movement of the pipe.

2.8.2.3 Where a pipe passes into a building it shall be arranged so as to accommodate differential movement and shall be accessible for withdrawal and replacement. Where a sleeve is used for this purpose, it shall be capable of resisting external loading and shall be sealed at each end in accordance with **2.8.2.2**. The diameter of the sleeve and the radius of any bends therein shall be such as to permit the ready insertion and withdrawal of the pipe (see figure 11).

2.8.2.4 No sleeve intended for carrying a water pipe shall contain within it any other pipe.

2.8.2.5 Pipes and pipe joints enclosed in a purpose-made chase in any external wall or located under a suspended floor at ground level or enclosed within a purpose-made sleeve or duct under any solid floor shall, where necessary, be wrapped, plastics-coated or otherwise protected from freezing, corrosion and thermal movement.

2.8.2.6 All pipes laid in ducts shall be adequately supported by fixing in accordance with **3.1.7.2**.

2.8.3 Underground stopvalves

stopvalves installed on an underground pipe shall be enclosed within a pipe guard or chamber under a surface box of the appropriate grade for the traffic loading according to the location (see BS 5834 : Part 2).

2.8.4 Accessibility of above ground valves

Every valve, including any backflow prevention device, shall be so placed that it is readily accessible for examination, maintenance and operation by the means by which it is designed to be operated. Any covers shall be fixed by removable fastenings.

2.8.5 Cisterns

Every storage cistern shall be so placed and equipped that the interior thereof can be inspected and cleansed and the float-operated valve can be maintained, as in figure 13. For this purpose a clear space of not less than 350 mm shall be provided between the top of the cistern and any ceiling or other obstruction above the cistern. In the case of small cisterns the overhead unobstructed space may be reduced to 225 mm provided no dimension of the cistern exceeds 450 mm in any plane.

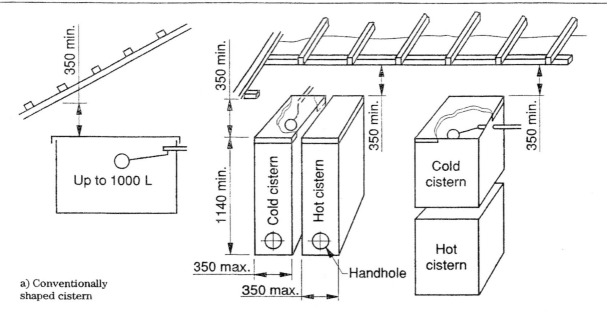

a) Conventionally
shaped cistern

NOTE. Acceptable sizes and positions of handholes are given
in clause **3** of BS 3198 : 1981

b) Plumbing units

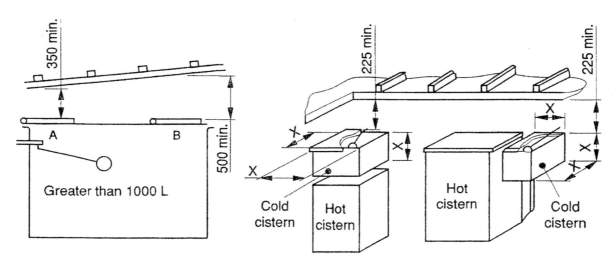

NOTE. A provides access to float valve
B provides access for inspection

Dimension X should not be greater than 450

c) Large capacity cistern with bolted-on lid

d) Hot water storage combination units

All dimensions are in millimetres

Figure 13. Clear space needed above storage cisterns

© BSI 1997

2.9 Water economy and energy conservation

2.9.1 General

The designer shall consider the water usage and energy costs of an installation and seek to minimize these, taking into account the requirements and recommendations of **2.9.2** for water usage and **2.9.3** for energy costs.

COMMENTARY AND RECOMMENDATIONS ON 2.9.1

Working pressure should be limited to the necessary maximum.

BS 6465 : Part 1 gives guidance on the selection of sanitary appliances and installations and should be considered in conjunction with the requirements and recommendations of 2.9.2.

2.9.2 Water economy

2.9.2.1 *Leakage*

Warning pipes from cisterns and discharge pipes from relief valves shall be located so that any discharge will be readily observed.

2.9.2.2 *WC flushing*

Every WC pan shall satisfy the flushing requirements of BS 5503 : Part 2 when used with the flushing apparatus installed.

COMMENTARY AND RECOMMENDATIONS ON 2.9.2.2

Attention is drawn to the water byelaws with respect to the arrangement of WC flushing (see A.2).

The discharge of the flushing apparatus should be related to the design of the pan and arbitrary reduction in the flush is not recommended.

2.9.2.3 *Urinal flushing*

Every urinal shall be flushed with water supplied by an automatic flushing cistern which incorporates siphonic apparatus.

Any cistern serving two or more urinal bowls or urinal slab positions shall be filled with water at a rate not exceeding 7.5 l/h per bowl or 700 mm width of urinal slab.

A cistern serving a single urinal shall be filled with water at a rate not exceeding 10 l/h.

COMMENTARY AND RECOMMENDATIONS ON 2.9.2.3

In lightly used installations, a user operated or actuated flush for individual stalls or bowls may be fitted and will show a water saving if each unit is used less frequently than the automatic flushing rate.

2.9.2.4 *Waste plugs*

Every waste outlet from a bath (other than a shower bath or shower tray), washbasin, sink or similar appliance shall be provided with a well-fitting plug and retaining chain, pop-up plug or an equally effective closure, except where the water supply is only by way of a fitting incapable of supplying water at a rate exceeding 3.6 l/min per appliance or per washing trough unit (see **2.9.2.6**), or the appliance is for medical, dental or veterinary use and is intended to be used with an unplugged waste.

2.9.2.5 *Self-closing taps*

Self-closing taps shall be non-concussive in operation and shall close against the prevailing water pressure without leakage.

COMMENTARY AND RECOMMENDATIONS ON 2.9.2.5

These taps are effective in preventing waste or undue consumption. They should, however, only be used where regular inspection and maintenance can be ensured.

2.9.2.6 *Washing troughs and fountains*

The fitting or fittings delivering water to a washing trough or fountain shall be capable of discharging to any one unit of the appliance without at the same time discharging to any other. A unit is taken to mean a length of not more than 600 mm of a straight trough or of the outer edge of a round appliance.

2.9.2.7 *Spray taps and aerators*

Spray taps and aerators shall be regularly maintained

COMMENTARY AND RECOMMENDATIONS ON 2.9.2.7

Spray taps may save as much as 50 % in both water consumption and fuel. The spray is only suitable for hand-rinsing and spray taps should not be used in situations where there may be heavy fouling of basins by grease and dirt. Without regular attention, the spray head is likely to become blocked over a period of time with any quality of water, but more particularly with hard water. Since self-cleansing velocities can rarely be satisfactorily achieved, particularly in long discharge pipes, blockage due to a build-up of grease and soap residue tend to occur, especially in soft water areas. Particularly good performances have been reported from areas with water in the range of 100 mg/l to 135 mg/l total hardness.

Aerators, although intended for the purpose of improving the flow pattern, may also reduce consumption by reducing the flow.

2.9.3 Energy conservation

2.9.3.1 *Hot water storage*

With the exception of certain solid fuel appliances, all hot water storage systems shall be fitted with a thermostat to control the maximum water temperature.

All pipes forming part of a primary or a secondary circulation system for supplying domestic hot water and all pipes carrying hot water to a tap or other outlet that are longer than the maximum length given in table 9, shall be thermally insulated in accordance with BS 5422, or so that the energy loss under normal operating conditions at no time exceeds the values given in table 10.

Table 9. Maximum recommended lengths of uninsulated hot water pipes

Outside diameter of pipe	Maximum length
mm	m
12	20
Over 12 up to and including 22	12
Over 22 up to and including 28	8
Over 28	3

Table 10. Maximum permitted rates of energy loss from pipes

Outside diameter of pipe[1]	Maximum energy loss
mm	W/m^2
10	675
20	400
30	280
40	220
50 and above	175

[1] For intermediate values of pipe diameter, the corresponding maximum energy loss is found by interpolation.

COMMENTARY AND RECOMMENDATION ON 2.9.3.1

The need to restrict the length of hot water distributing pipes is considered in 2.3.8..

If trace heating is used, it should be of the electric self-regulating type specifically formulated for domestic hot water systems. The system should conform to BS 6351.

Reducing the quantity and temperature of hot water heated and/or stored to those necessary to meet requirements will produce energy savings in addition to those achieved by insulation and controls. Storage vessels should therefore be sized to meet requirements without excessive over-capacity and consideration should be given to fitting devices, such as double element or twin electric immersion heaters or manually controlled economy valves on directly heated gas circulator systems, which enable a reduced quantity of water to be heated when desired.

2.9.3.2 *Pumping of cold water*

The energy cost of pumping shall be minimized by making prudent use of mains water pressure in consultation with the water supplier. Permission to install a pump on a supply pipe shall be obtained from the water supplier.

COMMENTARY AND RECOMMENDATIONS ON 2.9.3.2

Where mains pressure is insufficient to supply the upper floors of a building, mains supply to the lower floors without pumping should be considered.

                                                                       © BSI 1997

Section 3. Installation

3.1 Work on site

3.1.1 Handling of materials

3.1.1.1 General

All materials and components used for the construction of a water system shall be handled with sufficient care and attention to prevent their deterioration. Such deterioration may impair their serviceability or affect the performance of the system.

COMMENTARY AND RECOMMENDATIONS ON 3.1.1.1

Some pipes are manufactured from asbestos cement. Work on these pipes, in common with work on all asbestos containing materials, is subject to the Control of Asbestos at Work Regulations and the overriding duty to keep exposure to asbestos dust as low as is reasonably practicable. Asbestos cement pipes contain about 10 % white asbestos and may also contain 1 % brown asbestos. These pipes are generally safe to handle, but great care should be exercised in cutting and grinding operations to keep dust generated to the minimum and prevent people breathing in the dust. This may be achieved by the use of damping down and using hand rather than power tools. If in doubt, guidance should be sought from the Health and Safety Executive.

Manufacturers' advice should be followed concerning how their products should be loaded, transported, unloaded and stored. Pipes, fittings and components in any material should be handled carefully to reduce damage.

3.1.1.2 Bending of pipes

Damaged pipes shall be rejected.

COMMENTARY AND RECOMMENDATIONS ON 3.1.1.2

Care should be taken to avoid crimping and restricting the diameter of pipes when forming bends. Purpose-designed equipment should be used where appropriate.

3.1.2 Joining of pipes

3.1.2.1 General

All proprietary joints shall be made in accordance with the manufacturer's instructions. Care shall be taken to establish satisfactory jointing techniques for all water service pipework. When making joints by welding, brazing or soldering, precautions shall be taken to avoid the risk of fire, and care taken to avoid inhalation of fumes from the jointing process. All burrs shall be removed from the ends of pipes and any jointing materials used shall be prevented from entering the system. All piping and fittings shall be cleaned internally and shall be free from particles of sand, soil, metal filings and chips.

No metal pipe shall be connected to any other pipe or water fitting by means of an adhesive in any case where the metal pipe is:

   a) installed in the ground or passes through or under any wall footing or foundation;

   b) embedded in a wall or solid floor;

   c) enclosed in a chase or duct;

   d) in a position where access is difficult.

COMMENTARY AND RECOMMENDATIONS ON 3.1.2.1

Cutting tools that are in good condition should be used to limit tube distortion and the tube should be cut square with the axis.

Any tube ends that are distorted should be re-rounded using a suitable tool prior to the joint assembly.

3.1.2.2 Copper pipes

When making a capillary joint the mating faces of the tube and fitting shall be abrasively cleaned and an approved flux applied sparingly to the spigot.

The ends of annealed tubes shall always be re-rounded.

The type of fitting and jointing methods used shall be in accordance with table 11.

COMMENTARY AND RECOMMENDATIONS ON 3.1.2.2

Compression fittings: the non-manipulative type of compression joint, as its name implies, does not require any working of the tube end other than cutting square. The joint is made tight by means of a loose ring or sleeve that grips the outside wall of the tube when the coupling nut is tightened.

In the manipulative type of compression joint the end of the tube is flared, cupped or belled with special forming tools and is compressed by means of a coupling nut against a shaped end of corresponding section on the fitting or a loose thimble.

Capillary fittings: the joint should be heated until the solder, which is either constrained within the fitting (integral ring) or is fed in with a solder stick or wire (end feed), flows by capillary attraction to fill the joint space. The joint should remain untouched until the solder has cooled and solidified but then any surplus flux on the assembly should be carefully removed. Use of excessive amounts of flux should be avoided; sparing use on the spigot is recommended to avoid the flux entering the bore.

Table 11. Jointing of light gauge copper and stainless steel tube					
Tube	Fittings conforming to BS 864 : Part 2		Other methods		
	Compression type A non-manipulative[1]	Compression type B manipulative	Capillary (soft solder)	Brazing	Autogenous welding
Annealed copper tube conforming to table W of BS 2871 : Part 1 : 1971	Yes	Yes	Yes	Yes	Yes
Half-hard copper tube conforming to table X of BS 2871 : Part 1 : 1971	Yes	Yes	Yes	Yes	Yes
Annealed copper tube conforming to table Y of BS 2871 : Part 1 : 1971	No	Yes	Yes	Yes	Yes
Half-hard copper tube conforming to table Y of BS 2871 : Part 1 : 1971	Yes	Yes	Yes	Yes	Yes
Hard copper tube conforming to table Z of BS 2871 : Part 1 : 1971	Yes	No	Yes	No	No
Stainless steel tube conforming to BS 4127 : 1994	Yes	Yes	No	Yes	Yes
[1] Not to be used underground.					

3.1.2.2.1 Autogenous welding

Autogenous welded joints, either directly between tubes or using copper or copper alloy fittings suitable for welding, shall be made with a filler rod of copper or suitable zinc-free copper alloy together with a suitable flux.

3.1.2.2.2 Brazed joints

Brazed joints either using capillary type joints formed by special tools or using copper alloy fittings shall be made with a zinc-free silver brazing alloy with a suitable flux or copper phosphorus alloys.

3.1.2.3 Steel pipes

3.1.2.3.1 Welded joints shall not be used where a protective lining would be damaged by heat.

3.1.2.3.2 Screwed joints in steel piping shall be made with screwed socket joints using wrought-iron, steel or malleable cast-iron fittings. A thread filler shall be used. Exposed threads left after jointing shall be painted or, where installed underground, thickly coated with bituminous or other suitable corrosion preventative in accordance with BS 5493.

3.1.2.3.3 Flange joints shall be made with screwed or welded flanges of steel or cast-iron using jointing rings and, if necessary, a suitable jointing paste.

COMMENTARY AND RECOMMENDATIONS TO 3.1.2.3

The nuts should be carefully tightened, in opposite pairs, until the jointing ring is sufficiently compressed between the flanges for a watertight joint.

3.1.2.4 Stainless steel pipes

3.1.2.4.1 Compression fittings

Compression joints on plain ended stainless steel tube shall be made with copper alloy or stainless steel compression fittings. (See table 11.)

3.1.2.4.2 Capillary fittings

Capillary joints on plain ended stainless steel tube shall be made with copper, copper alloy or stainless steel fittings using silver solder or silver brazing, but not soft solder.

3.1.2.5 Unplasticized PVC pipes

3.1.2.5.1 Mechanical joints

Mechanical joints in unplasticized PVC piping of nominal diameter DN 2 and upwards shall be made in accordance with BS 4346 : Part 2, by the use of push-fit integral elastomeric sealing rings which are compressed when the plain ended pipes are inserted into the adjoining sockets. The plain pipe ends shall be chamfered and the surfaces cleaned and lubricated. The chamfered pipe end shall be inserted fully into the adjoining socket (except where provision is to be made for expansion) or as far as any locating mark put on the spigot end by the manufacturer. The sealing rings shall conform to BS 2494.

3.1.2.5.2 Compression joints

Compression joints shall only be used with unplasticized PVC piping of nominal diameter DN 2 and smaller. The joints shall be of the non-manipulative type. Care shall be taken to avoid over-tightening.

© BSI 1997

3.1.2.5.3 Solvent cement welded joints

Solvent cement welded joints in unplasticized PVC piping shall be made using a solvent cement conforming to BS 4346 : Part 3 recommended by the manufacturer of the pipe. The dimensions of the spigots and sockets shall conform to BS 4346 : Part 1 and reference shall be made to CP 312 : Part 2 for jointing methods.

NOTE. Joints may also be made using integral sockets formed in the pipes and solvent cemented.

3.1.2.5.4 Flanged joints

Flanged joints used for connections to valves and fittings shall use full-face flanges or stub-flange, both with corrosion resistant or immune backing rings and bolting.

3.1.2.6 Polyethylene pipes

3.1.2.6.1 Mechanical joints shall be made in accordance with CP 312 using either plastics or metal proprietary compression fittings, e.g. brass, gun metal or malleable iron. These shall include liners to support the bore of the pipe except where the manufacturer of the fitting instructs otherwise.

3.1.2.6.2 To ensure satisfactory jointing of the materials from which the pipe and fittings are made compatibility shall be established. The manufacturer's instructions shall be carefully followed.

No attempt shall be made to joint polyethylene piping by solvent cement welding.

3.1.2.7 Polybutylene pipes

Mechanical joints in polybutylene pipes conforming to BS 7291 : Part 2 shall be made using fittings conforming to the same standard.

3.1.3 Connections between different materials

3.1.3.1 Above ground pipework

When different materials are used within a single installation the method of jointing shall be designed for both materials, for the safety and integrity of the system.

COMMENTARY AND RECOMMENDATIONS
ON 3.1.3.1

Adaptor couplings are available for this purpose covering a range of different jointing methods and including both direct and union type couplings; these should be used whenever possible. Where suitable adaptors are not available for the particular joint required both materials should be adapted to BSP threaded ends which should be screwed together, if male and female, or should be connected by a nipple, socket or union.

3.1.3.2 Below-ground pipework

Joints in buried pipework shall be kept to the absolute minimum and joints between pipes of different materials shall be restricted to connections between large supply pipes similar to suppliers' mains and pipes serving individual buildings, such as will occur on large sites only.

Service connections to cast iron pipes shall be made by drilling and tapping the pipe and screwing in a copper alloy union ferrule.

For making service connections to unplasticized PVC pipes, a saddle shall be fixed round the larger pipe and a ferrule screwed into the saddle. Installers shall observe the manufacturer's instructions. In the case of fibre cement pipes the same method shall be used or a proprietary threadless ferrule shall be used in accordance with the manufacturer's instructions.

Service connections to PE pipes shall be made using either a saddle fusion fitting (for PE service pipes only) or a self-tapping saddle.

3.1.4 Joining pipes to cisterns and tanks

3.1.4.1 General

Cisterns and tanks shall be properly supported to avoid undue stress on the pipe connections and deformation of the cistern or tank when filled. Holes shall be correctly aligned for the connection of pipes to cisterns and tanks. All debris shall be removed from the inside of the cistern or tank before filling.

3.1.4.2 Steel pipes to steel or glass reinforced cisterns and tanks

The threaded end of the pipe shall be secured in the hole in the cistern or tank either by backnuts and washers both inside and outside (soft washers being used additionally with glass reinforced plastics cisterns and tanks or where there are irregular surfaces) or by using bolted or welded flanged connections.

3.1.4.3 Copper or plastics pipe to steel, or glass reinforced plastics cisterns and tanks

A copper alloy connector having a shoulder to bear on the outside of the cistern or tank and secured by a backnut to the inside shall be used. Corrosion resistant support washers shall be used both on the inside and the outside of the cistern or tank; additional soft washers shall be used as in 3.1.4.2.

3.1.4.4 Concrete cisterns and tanks

Connections to concrete cisterns and tanks shall be made with short thread flanged connections having a puddle flange either cast or welded on. Connections shall be properly aligned both in the horizontal and vertical planes when being cast into the concrete, which shall be compacted around the puddle flange to ensure a watertight joint.

3.1.4.5 Thermoplastics cisterns

Holes cut for pipes shall be circular, have clean edges and be free from notches. There shall not be any residual scribe lines after the hole is cut.

Where a jointing sealant is required it shall conform to BS 6956 : Part 5.

A supporting back plate shall be used on the outside of the cistern where the float-operated valve is fitted, to spread the thrust of the lever arm over a greater area of the side wall. Corrosion resistant support washers shall be used both on the inside and the outside of the cistern with additional soft washers.

3.1.5 Underground pipe laying

3.1.5.1 *General*

Pipes shall be laid to ensure even support throughout their length and shall not rest on their sockets or on bricks, tiles or other makeshift supports. Plastics pipes shall be laid in accordance with CP 312 :
Parts 1, 2 and 3 on a bed free from sharp stones.

COMMENTARY AND RECOMMENDATIONS
ON 3.1.5.1

Pipes should be laid true to line to the general contours of the ground and at a sufficient depth for the pipe diameter to allow for the minimum cover below finished ground level (see 2.1.8).

3.1.5.2 Trench excavations

The bottom of trench excavations shall be carefully prepared to a firm even surface so that the barrels of the pipes when laid are well bedded for their whole length. Mud, rock projections, boulders, hard spots and local soft spots shall be removed and replaced with selected fill material consolidated to the required level.

Where rock is encountered, the trench shall be cut at least 150 mm deeper than other ground and made up with well rammed material.

3.1.5.3 *Trench backfilling*

When backfilling trenches the pipes shall be surrounded with suitable material consolidated to resist subsequent movement of the pipes.

No large stones or sharp objects shall be in contact with the pipes.

3.1.5.4 *Ingress of dirt*

Pipes shall be kept clean and, immediately before laying each pipe and fitting, shall be thoroughly cleansed internally and the open end temporarily capped until jointing takes place. Care shall be taken to keep the joint surfaces clean. After laying and jointing, the leading end shall remain capped.

COMMENTARY AND RECOMMENDATIONS
ON 3.1.5.4

Precautions should be taken to prevent flotation of the capped pipes, in case the trench becomes flooded.

3.1.5.5 *Protective coatings*

Coatings, sheathings or wrappings shall be examined for damage, repaired where necessary, and made continuous before trench excavations are backfilled.

3.1.5.6 *Restraint of pipes*

Except where the method of joining and normal trench backfill are adequate to prevent longitudinal movement, pipe restraints designed to resist the thrusts produced by the test pressure to be applied shall be installed at all changes of direction and blank ends. The magnitudes of these thrusts, which act in the directions shown in figure 14, shall be calculated as follows.

End thrust (in kN) = 100 AP

Radial thrust at bends (in kN) = 100 $AP \times 2\sin \theta/2$

where

A is the cross-sectional area of the inside of socket (in m^2);

P is the test pressure (in bar);

θ is the angle of deviation of bend.

Alternatively, when standard fittings are used, the thrusts shall be calculated by multiplying the values given in table 12 by the test pressure (bar).

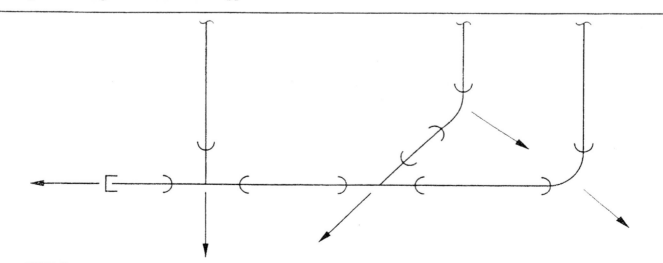

NOTE. Figure 14 is based on a figure taken from the *Plumbing engineering services design guide* [9], by kind permission of the Institute of Plumbing.

Figure 14. Directions of thrusts developed in a pipeline due to internal pressure

© BSI 1997

Table 12. Thrust per bar internal pressure					
Nominal internal diameter of pipe	End thrust	Radial thrust on bends of angle kN			
mm		90°	45°	22¼°	11¼°
50	0.38	0.53	0.29	0.15	0.07
75	0.72	1.02	0.55	0.28	0.15
100	1.17	1.66	0.90	0.46	0.24
125	1.76	2.49	1.35	0.69	0.35
150	2.47	3.50	1.89	0.96	0.49
175	3.29	4.66	2.52	1.29	0.65
200	4.24	5.99	3.24	1.66	0.84
225	5.27	7.46	4.04	2.06	1.04
250	6.43	9.09	4.92	2.51	1.26
300	9.38	13.26	7.18	3.66	1.84
350	12.53	17.71	9.59	4.89	2.46

Thrust blocks for the restraint of pipelines shall have adequate bearing area to resist the thrust, calculated using the data given in table 13 or on measurements of soil bearing capacity for horizontal thrusts, made on site.

Table 13. Bearing capacity of soils	
Soil type	Safe bearing load kN/m²
Soft clay	24
Sand	48
Sandstone and gravel	72
Sand and gravel bonded with clay	96
Shale	240

3.1.5.7 *Valve chambers and surface boxes*

Surface boxes shall be provided to give access to operate valves and hydrants, and shall be supported on concrete or brickwork which shall not be allowed to rest on the pipes and transmit loads to them, allowance being made for settlement.

Alternatively, vertical guard pipes or precast concrete sections shall be provided to enclose the spindles of valves.

Brick or concrete hydrant chambers shall be constructed of sufficient dimensions to permit repairs.

3.1.6 Branch connections for buildings

3.1.6.1 *Contamination*

Precautions to avoid contamination of the supply pipe shall be taken when making a connection. Where there has been a possibility of contamination, the pipe shall be subsequently disinfected.

3.1.6.2 *Building entry*

Underground pipes entering a building shall do so at the level given in 2.7.2.2 (see also 2.8).

Where a pipe enters a building it shall be accommodated in a sleeve that has previously been solidly built in and the space between the pipe and the sleeve shall be filled with non-hardening, non-cracking, water-resistant material for a minimum length of 150 mm at both ends to prevent the passage of water, gas or vermin. (See 2.7.2.2 and figure 11).

3.1.7 Pipework in buildings

3.1.7.1 *Allowance for thermal movement*

In installations that do not have limited straight runs and many bends and offsets, allowance for expansion and contraction of the pipes shall be made by forming expansion loops, by introducing changes of direction to avoid long straight runs or by fitting proprietary expansion joints.

COMMENTARY AND RECOMMENDATIONS ON 3.1.7.1

This is particularly important where temperature changes are considerable (e.g. hot water distribution pipework) and where the pipe material has a relatively large coefficient of thermal expansion (e.g. plastics). In installations with limited straight runs and many bends and offsets, thermal movement is accommodated.

3.1.7.2 *Spacings for pipe fixings*

The spacings for fixings for internally located piping shall be in accordance with table 14.

3.1.7.3 *Fixings for copper and stainless steel pipe*

Copper and stainless steel piping shall be secured by copper, copper alloy or plastics clips or brackets.

3.1.7.4 *Fixings for steel pipe*

Steel piping shall be secured by steel, copper alloy, suitable plastics clips or brackets. Copper clips or brackets shall not be used for fixing steel piping.

3.1.7.5 *Fixings for iron pipe*

Iron pipe shall be secured by heavy weight holderbats of iron or low carbon steel either built in or bolted to the structure.

3.1.7.6 *Fixings for plastics pipes*

Plastics piping shall be secured by suitable metallic or plastics clips or brackets. Allowance shall be made for free lateral movement within the clips and brackets.

3.1.7.7 *Fixings for insulated piping*

Piping that is to be insulated shall be secured on clips or brackets that allow sufficient space behind the pipe and the surface to which the pipe is fixed for the insulation to be properly installed.

3.1.7.8 *Concealed piping*

Piping shall be housed in ducts or wall chases and have access for maintenance and inspection.

COMMENTARY AND RECOMMENDATIONS 3.1.7.8 Ducts and chases should be constructed as the building structure is erected and should be finished to receive pipe fixings.

Table 14. Maximum spacing of fixing for internal piping

Type of piping	Nominal diameter of pipe DN mm		Spacing on horizontal run m	Spacing on vertical run m
Copper conforming to tables X and Z of BS 2871 : Part 1 : 1971 and stainless steel conforming to BS 4127 : Part 2 : 1972	15		1.2	1.8
	22		1.8	2.4
	28		1.8	2.4
	35		2.4	3.0
	42		2.4	3.0
	54		2.7	3.0
	67		3.0	3.6
	76		3.0	3.6
	108		3.0	3.6
	133		3.0	3.6
	159		3.6	4.2
	Copper	Steel		
Copper conforming to: table Y of BS 2871 Part 1 : 1971 and steel conforming to BS 4127 : Part 2	15	15	1.8	2.0
	22	20	2.4	3.0
	28	25	2.4	3.0
	35	32	2.7	3.0
	42	40	3.0	3.6
	54	50	3.0	3.6
	67	65	3.0	3.6
	76	80	3.6	4.5
	108	100	3.9	4.5
Ductile iron conforming to BS EN 545, BS EN 598 and BS EN 969.	80		2.7	2.7
	100		2.7	2.7
	150		3.6	3.6

© BSI 1997

Table 14. Maximum spacing of fixing for internal piping (*continued*)

Type of piping	Nominal diameter of pipe DN mm	Spacing on horizontal run m	Spacing on vertical run m
Unplasticized polyvinyl chloride (PVC-U)[1] conforming to BS 3505	$\frac{1}{4}$	0.6	1.1
	$\frac{1}{2}$	0.7	1.3
	$\frac{3}{4}$	0.7	1.4
	1	0.8	1.6
	$1\frac{1}{4}$	0.9	1.7
	$1\frac{1}{2}$	1.0	1.9
	2	1.1	2.2
	3	1.4	2.8
	4	1.6	3.1
	6	1.9	3.7
Black MDPE pipe conforming to BS 6730	20	0.5	0.9
	25	0.6	1.2
	32	0.6	1.2
	50	0.8	1.5
	63	0.8	1.6
Chlorinated polyvinyl chloride (PVC-C)[2] conforming to BS 7291 : Parts 1 and 4	12 to 25	0.5	1.0
	32 to 63	0.8	2.2
Polybutylene (PB) and cross-linked polyethylene (PE-X)[2] conforming to BS 7291 : Parts 2 and 3	Up to 16	0.3	0.5
	18 to 25	0.5	0.8
	2S	0.8	1.0
	32	0.9	1.2
	35	0.9	1.2

[1] Figures are for normal ambient temperatures below 20 °C. For temperatures above 20 °C the pipe manufacturer should be consulted.

[2] Based on water temperature up to 80 °C.

3.1.7.9 *Piping passing through structural timbers*

Strutural timbers shall not be notched or bored in such a way that the integrity of the structure is compromised.

COMMENTARY AND RECOMMENDATIONS ON 3.1.7.9

Structural timbers should only be notched or bored with the permission of, and as directed by, the architect, structural engineer and/or supervising officer for the building. Notches and holes should be as small as necessary to receive pipes. Whenever possible, notches should be U shaped and formed by parallel cuts to previously bored holes.

It is essential that structural members are not weakened by indiscriminate notching and boring. In this respect the positions are as important as the sizes of notches and holes. Notches and holes in timber beams and joists should only be made according to dimensions shown in figure 15.

3.1.7.10 *Clearance of structural members*

Piping laid through notches, holes, cut-outs or chases shall not be subjected to external forces and shall be free to expand or contract. Pipe sleeves shall be provided where piping passes through walls and floors.

3.1.7.11 *Penetration of fire walls and floors*

Penetration of compartment walls and floors and fire barriers shall be fire-stopped to prevent the passage of smoke and flame, (see **A.1**).

3.1.8 Electrical bonding

No water pipe shall be used as an electrode for earthing purposes, but all metal pipes shall be bonded to the electrical installation main earth terminal as near as possible to the point of entry into the building (see **2.2.8.3** and **4.2.5**.)

3.1.9 Taps

Taps not fixed directly to an appliance shall be screwed into a suitable pipe fitting and the fitting, or the pipe immediately adjacent to the tap, shall be firmly secured to a suitable support, so as to prevent strain on the pipe and its joints when the tap is operated.

COMMENTARY AND RECOMMENDATIONS ON 3.1.9

The use of a backplate elbow to receive the tap and a wall flange plugged and screwed to the wall or support is preferred.

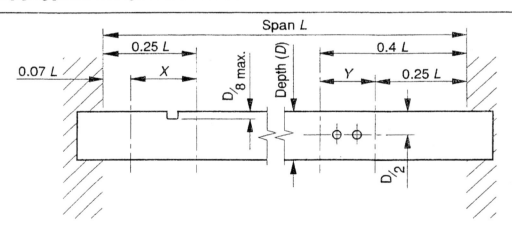

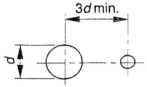

Spacing of holes

NOTE.

X is the allowable limits of location for cut notches, to be in either the top or bottom surface, not both.

Y is the allowable location for drilled holes.

d is the diameter of the larger of two adjacent holes.

The diameter (d) shall not exceed $\dfrac{D}{4}$.

Figure 15. Recommended positions of notches and holes in timber beams and joists

© BSI 1997

3.1.10 Flushing and disinfection

3.1.10.1 *Flushing*

Every new water service, cistern, distributing pipe, hot water cylinder or other appliance and any extension or modification to such a service shall be thoroughly flushed with drinking water before being taken into use. Where a system is not brought into use immediately after commissioning and it has not been flushed at regular intervals (up to 30 days depending on the characteristics of the water), it shall be disinfected before bringing into use.

3.1.10.2 *Disinfection*

After flushing, systems shall be disinfected in accordance with **3.1.10.3** to **3.1.10.5** in the following situations:

a) in new installations (except private dwellings occupied by a single family);

b) where major extensions or alterations have been carried out;

c) where underground pipework has been installed (except where localized repairs only have been carried out or junctions have been inserted (see **3.1.10.6**);

d) where it is suspected that contamination may have occurred, e.g. fouling by sewage, drainage, animals or physical entry by site personnel for interior inspection, painting or repairs;

e) where a system has not been in regular use and not regularly flushed.

Where any pipework under mains pressure or upstream of any back-flow prevention device within the installation is to be disinfected, the water supplier shall be informed.

Chemicals used for disinfection of drinking water installations shall be those that are listed in the Drinking Water Inspectorate's *List of substances, products and processes approved under regulations 25 and 26 for use in connection with the supply of water for drinking, washing, cooking or food production purposes*, Sections 4 and 5, which is published in part 4 of *the Water fittings and materials directory* [1].

Where water that has been used to disinfect an installation is to be discharged into a sewer, the authority responsible for that sewer shall be informed prior to discharge.

Where this water is to be discharged into a water course or into a drain leading to the same, a consent to discharge shall be obtained from the appropriate authority; that is, the National Rivers Authority (NRA) in England and Wales, the Scottish Environmental Protection Agency in Scotland and the Department of the Environment for Northern Ireland in Northern Ireland.

The sequence of disinfection shall be water mains, service pipes cisterns and the internal distribution system.

COMMENTARY AND RECOMMENDATIONS ON 3.1.10.2

Flushing and disinfection are not a substitute for a high degree of cleanliness during installation. (See also 3.1.5.4.)

For single dwellings and minor extensions or alterations in any premises, flushing is all that is normally required, unless contamination is suspected.

3.1.10.3 *Safety*

Systems, or parts of systems, shall not be used during the disinfection procedure and all outlets shall be marked with 'DISINFECTION IN PROGRESS, DO NOT USE'.

To avoid the generation of toxic fumes, no other chemicals, like toilet cleansers shall be added to the water until disinfection is complete.

All building users shall be informed of the disinfection before it takes place. This includes those users not normally in attendance during working hours, i.e. cleaners and security guards.

3.1.10.4 *Disinfection procedure*

The system to be disinfected shall be thoroughly flushed prior to commencement of the disinfection procedure.

3.1.10.4.1 *Methods using chlorine as a disinfectant*

The system shall be filled with chlorinated water at an initial concentration of 50 mg/l (50 p.p.m) for a contact period of 1 h. If the free residual chlorine measured at the end of the contact period is less than 30 mg/l (30 p.p.m) the disinfection process shall be repeated.

After successful chlorination, the system shall be immediately drained and thoroughly flushed with clean water. Flushing shall continue until the free residual chlorine is at the level present in the drinking water supplied.

3.1.10.4.2 *Methods using approved disinfectants other than chlorine*

The system shall be filled with the approved disinfectant solution at the initial concentration and for the contact time specified by the manufacturer. If the residual of the approved disinfectant at the end of the contact time is less than the manufacturer's recommendation, the disinfection procedure shall be repeated.

After successful disinfection, the system shall be immediately drained and thoroughly flushed with clean water. Flushing shall continue in accordance with the disinfectant manufacturer's instructions/recommendations or until there is no evidence of the disinfectant chemical being present, or it is at a level that is no higher than that present in the drinking water supplied.

3.1.10.4.3 *Post disinfection*

After flushing, a sample(s) for bacteriological analysis shall be taken, and analysed, under the supervision of a microbiologist, who shall also determine the number and method of collection of samples.

Where a bacteriological analysis of the samples indicates that adequate disinfection has not been achieved, the installation shall be flushed, re-disinfected and further samples taken.

COMMENTARY AND RECOMMENDATIONS
ON 3.1.10.4

Provided there is no suspicion that the system has been fouled by sewage, drainage or animals prior to disinfection, the installation may be put into service before the result of the bacteriological analysis is known.

For supply pipes (including unvented hot water systems off the supply pipe) and after flushing, disinfectant solution should be injected through a properly installed injection point at the upstream end of the supply pipe, until the disinfectant solution discharged at the downstream end of the pipeline is equal to the initial concentration; the contact period then commences.

In gravity distribution systems within buildings, one method of introducing disinfectant solution is as follows:

After flushing, the system should be filled with water and the servicing valve on the supply to the cistern closed. The capacity of the cistern should be assessed and a calculated quantity of disinfectant solution of known strength should be added to the cistern to give the initial concentration of disinfectant solution in the cistern. The disinfectant solution should be drawn around the system by successively opening each draw-off fitting, working away from the cistern, and closing it when disinfectant solution at the initial concentration is discharged, (as determined by using colorimetric methods, where possible). The cistern should be refilled and disinfected as above as necessary during this operation, maintaining the initial concentration of disinfectant solution in the cistern at all times. The contact time should commence when the entire system is filled with disinfectant solution, including the cistern, up to overflow level.

Irrespective of the method of disinfection, the contact time commences when the entire system, including the cistern up to overflow level, is full of disinfectant solution at the required initial concentration.

3.1.10.5 *Cisterns with internal coatings*

Because high chlorine concentrations and other disinfectants can adversely affect new coatings in cisterns and release chlorinated or other compounds into the water the coating shall be thoroughly cured before disinfection takes place and care shall be taken not to exceed 50 mg/l chlorine concentration or, in the case of an alternative approved disinfectant, the manufacturer's recommendation.

3.1.10.6 *Localized repairs*

Junctions, or fittings for a localized repair, inserted into an existing external pipeline shall be disinfected by immersion in a solution of sodium hypochlorite containing 200 mg/l of available chlorine. Where other disinfectants are used the concentration shall be in accordance with the manufacturer's recommendations.

3.1.11 Identifying and recording piping locations

3.1.11.1 *Location of pipes and valves*

Location and position of underground pipes and valves shall be recorded.

Surface boxes shall be marked to indicate what service is below them. Durable markers with stamped or set-in indexes shall be set up to indicate the pipe service, the size, the position and depth below the surface.

Indicator plates for hydrants shall conform to BS 3251.

COMMENTARY AND RECOMMENDATIONS
ON 3.1.11.1

Marker tapes are available for use and are generally laid a short distance above the pipe in the trench.

3.1.11.2 *Identification of above ground piping*

In any building other than a single dwelling:

a) water piping shall be colour banded and coded in accordance with BS 1710;

b) every supply pipe and every pipe for supplying water solely for fire fighting purposes shall be clearly and indelibly marked to distinguish them from each other and from every other pipe in the building.

3.1.11.3 *Record drawings*

During the installation of a water supply system, records of all pipe runs, cisterns, valves and outlets, shall be kept. On completion of the works, record drawings of the completed installation shall be prepared. These shall be handed to the owner of the building.

3.1.11.4 *Identification of valves and cisterns installed above ground*

All valves in hot and cold water services pipework and cisterns installed above ground shall be provided with an identification label, either secured by non-corrodible, incombustible means to the valve or fixed to a permanent structure near the valve. Labels secured to valves shall be of non-corrodible and incombustible material permanently and clearly marked, e.g. by stamping or engraving, with a description of the service concerned and the function of the valve. Alternatively, the label shall be marked with a reference number for the valve, instead of or in addition to the marking described in this subclause, and a durable diagram of the service, showing the valve reference numbers shall be fixed in a readily visible position to a permanent part of the building or structure. Labels fixed near valves shall conform to the requirements for labels secured to valves except that they need not be incombustible.

© BSI 1997

COMMENTARY AND RECOMMENDATIONS
ON 3.1.11.4

In order that the identify and function of each valve in a system can be readily assessed, it is recommended that a diagrammatic drawing is provided for every installation.

3.1.12 Inspection testing and commissioning of installations

3.1.12.1 *Procedure*

3.1.12.1.1 *General*

Inspections and tests shall be undertaken as installation proceeds, and on completion.

Prior notice shall be given to the water supplier before any statutory inspections or tests are undertaken.

Records of all tests undertaken shall be kept by the installer and handed over to the client on completion.

3.1.12.1.2 *Timing of tests*

The timing of tests shall be as follows:

a) *interim tests*: as soon as practicable after completion of the particular section, with particular attention to all work which will be concealed;

b) *final tests*: to be carried out on completion of all work on the water system and prior to handing over.

COMMENTARY AND RECOMMENDATIONS
ON 3.1.12.1.2

Satisfactory completion of an interim test does not constitute a final test.

3.1.12.1.3 *Re-tests*

Items failing any test shall be corrected immediately and re-tested before further work proceeds.

3.1.12.2 *Inspection*

Visual inspections by the water supplier shall be carried out at both interim and final testing before work is concealed, in order to detect faults in construction or materials.

All internal pipework shall be inspected to ensure that it has been securely fixed.

All cisterns, tanks, hot water cylinders and water heaters shall be inspected to ensure that they are properly supported and secured, that they are clean and free from swarf and that cisterns are provided with correctly fitting covers before testing takes place.

Unvented hot water storage installations shall be notified to the local authority to verify that they conform to building regulations (see **A.1**).

Before accepting a pipeline, a check shall be made that valve and hydrant boxes are aligned, that operating keys are provided for the valves and, in the case of deep valves, that extension spindles are installed.

COMMENTARY AND RECOMMENDATIONS
ON 3.1.12.2

In the case of visual inspection of underground pipework, particular attention should be paid to the pipe bed, the line and level of the pipe, irregularities at joints, the correct fitting of air valves, washout valves, sluice valves and other valves together with any other mains equipment specified, including the correct installation of thrust blocks where required, to ensure that protective coatings are undamaged.

Trenches should be inspected to ensure that excavation is to the correct depth to guard against frost and mechanical damage due to traffic, ploughing or agricultural activities.

No part of the pipe trench should be backfilled until these conditions have been satisfied and the installation seen to conform to the drawings and specifications and the appropriate byelaws and regulations.

3.1.12.3 *Hydraulic testing*

Defects revealed by any of the following tests shall be remedied and the tests repeated until a satisfactory result is obtained.

If the water is obtained from the water supplier's mains it shall be taken in accordance with the supplier's requirements.

3.1.12.3.1 *Testing of underground pipelines*

The installation to be tested shall be inspected for compliance with the drawings and specifications. Significant variations shall be investigated and corrected, if required, before proceeding with the test.

After laying, jointing and anchoring, the underground pipeline shall be slowly and carefully filled with water so that all air is expelled and then tested under pressure in accordance with clauses **3.1.12.3.3** or **3.1.12.3.4**, depending on the material from which the pipeline is constructed. The system shall be subjected to twice the maximum working pressure of the pipeline.

When water from the water supplier's mains is used for filling the pipeline under test, the main shall be disconnected from the pipeline before the test is begun. To avoid the risk of contamination, water used for testing shall be obtained from a drinking supply.

COMMENTARY AND RECOMMENDATIONS
ON 3.1.12.3.1

Long pipelines should be tested in sections as the work proceeds.

Final tests should be carried out only when all relevant work is complete. Completion for buried pipelines includes backfilling, compaction and surface finish.

Generally the tests are conducted immediately prior to the date of hand-over. Where long lengths of buried pipelines are laid clear of the general construction area, it may be practicable to carry out final tests for completed sections as work proceeds.

The whole installation, or where the work is phased the whole installation for each phase, is tested at this time, irrespective of satisfaction with interim tests.

If the pipeline is not below paved areas, heavy traffic is not allowed over the surface after final test.

A higher test pressure may be required in the case of any pumping main subject to surge.

3.1.12.3.2 *Testing of installations within buildings*

The installation shall be filled slowly with drinking water to allow air to be expelled from the system.

The complete installation shall be inspected for leaks.

The installation shall be tested hydraulically by subjecting the pipes, pipe fittings and connected appliances to a test pressure of not less than 1.5 times the maximum working pressure in accordance with clauses **3.1.12.3.3** or **3.1.12.3.4**, depending on the materials from which the pipeline is constructed. There shall be no visible leakage of water and the pressure shall be maintained for 1 h.

3.1.12.3.3 *Test procedure for rigid pipes*

The pipework shall be vented, filled slowly with drinking water and subjected to the required test pressure.

Where there are significant differences (>10 K) between the ambient temperature and the water temperature, there is an initial period of 30 min before the commencement of the test period, to permit temperature equilibrium after the test pressure has been applied. There shall be no visible leakage of water and the pressure shall be maintained for a test period of 1 h.

3.1.12.3.4 *Test procedure for elastomeric pipes*

The installer shall use test procedure A or B for the pressure testing of elastomeric pipes.

The pipework shall be vented and filled slowly with drinking water.

Test procedure A

a) Apply the required test pressure by pumping, in accordance with figure 16, for a period of 30 min. Inspect the pipework to identify any visible leaks in the system.

b) Reduce the pressure in the pipework by bleeding water from the system to 0.5 times the maximum working pressure.

c) Close the bleed valve. If the pressure remains at, or greater than, 0.5 times the maximum working pressure the system is regarded as leaktight. Visually check for leakage and monitor for 90 min. The test criteria are met if there is no reduction in pressure.

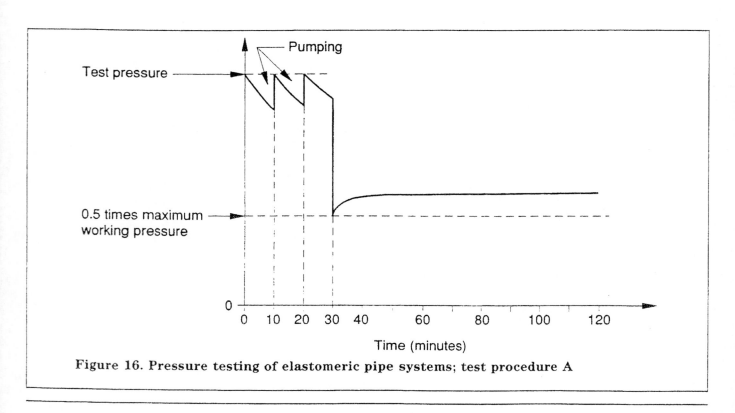

Figure 16. Pressure testing of elastomeric pipe systems; test procedure A

© BSI 1997

Test procedure B

a) Apply the required test pressure by pumping, in accordance with figure 17, for a period of 30 min and note the pressure in the pipeline at the end of the period. Inspect the pipework to identify any visible leaks in the system. Continue the test without further pumping.

b) Note the pressure after a further 30 min. If the pressure drop is less than 60 kPa (0.6 bar), the system can be considered to have no obvious leakage.

c) Visually check for leakage and monitor for 120 min. The test criteria are met if the pressure drop in the system is less than 20 kPa (0.2 bar).

COMMENTARY AND RECOMMENDATIONS ON 3.1.12.3.4

Test procedures A and B may also be used where the installation comprises both elastomeric and rigid pipes. When not stated otherwise the installer may choose either test procedure A or B.

3.1.12.4 *Connection to water supply system*

When all inspections and tests have been successfully completed and the system accepted from the installer, the water supplier shall be informed that the system is available for permanent connection to the supply.

COMMENTARY AND RECOMMENDATIONS ON 3.1.12.5

Each draw-off tap, shower fitting and float-operated valve should be checked for rate of flow against the specified requirements. Performance tests should also be carried out on any connected specialist items to show that they meet the requirements detailed in the specification.

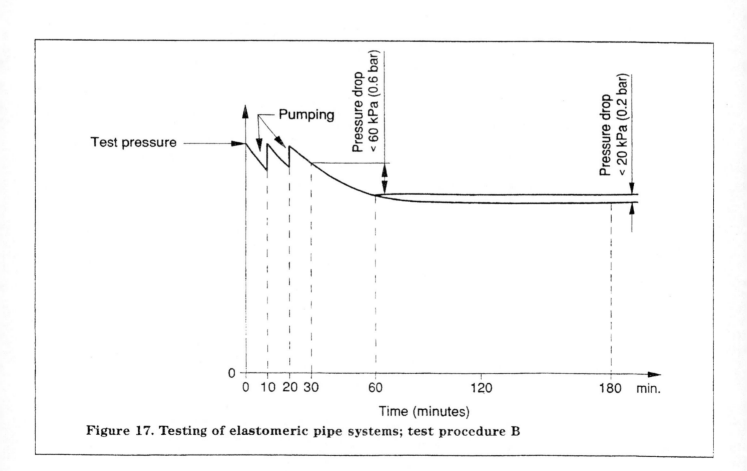

Figure 17. Testing of elastomeric pipe systems; test procedure B

Section 4. Maintenance

4.1 Maintenance procedures

Maintenance procedures shall be adopted to maintain the performance of the installation at the level specified in this standard for the original design and installation.

Unvented hot water storage installations shall be maintained and repaired only by a competent person (see building regulations **A.1**).

COMMENTARY AND RECOMMENDATIONS ON 4.1

The degree of formalization of maintenance required depends upon the size and utilization of the installation although the principles involved apply to all installations.

Maintenance of ducts would not normally apply to single dwellings but other requirements should be satisfied by the owner of the building.

In single dwellings the responsibility for maintenance normally rests on the householders who should pay attention to apparent leakages and should note any discharges from overflow pipes or regular discharges from any valves.

The owner of the building should have been provided with maintenance instructions and an accurate drawing of the installation, particularly showing where pipe runs are concealed. Control valves should be clearly labelled (see 3.1.11.4). Care should be taken to renew or protect labels when redecorating. Any alterations should be recorded on inspection, and a check made that these do not introduce undesirable features or contravene statutory requirements.

The services of a competent person should be obtained to carry out maintenance and repairs. Competence includes the appropriate skills and a knowledge of the relevant statutory requirements relating to water supply.

4.2 General

4.2.1 Inspection

In other than single dwellings, the installation shall be inspected periodically. Faults noticed on inspection shall be attended to immediately.

COMMENTARY AND RECOMMEDATIONS ON 4.2.1

The need for formalized inspection and records depends upon the size, type and complexity of the installation but in principle every installation should be inspected at least once per year in addition to any statutory inspections. Checks should be made that the appropriate back-siphonage prevention devices and relief valves are fitted where required.

4.2.2 Preventative maintenance

Manufacturer's recommendations or instructions regarding planned preventative maintenance of meters, pumps, treatment plant and similar equipment shall be followed.

4.2.3 Waste prevention

Attention shall be paid to rectify any instances of waste or undue consumption of water revealed by inspections or during maintenance operations.

COMMETARY AND RECOMMENDATIONS ON 4.2.3

In the case of metered installations the water meter provides an easy means of monitoring consumption. The meter or meters should be read at regular intervals and appropriate action taken if an unexplained increase in consumption is indicated.

4.2.4 Water analysis

In other than single dwellings regular analyses of water samples at intervals not exceeding 6 months shall be carried out wherever drinking water is stored.

COMMENTARY AND RECOMMENDATIONS ON 4.2.4

Periodic chemical and bacteriological analysis of water samples is a useful guide to the condition of an installation. The collection and analysis of water samples is particularly recommended for new installations in large buildings or complexes and where extensive repairs or alterations have been carried out to such installations.

4.2.5 Earthing and bonding

Where pipework, fittings or appliances are to be replaced, continuity of earthing and equipotential bonding shall be maintained (see **2.2.8.3** and **3.1.8**). Where pipework has been used for earthing, alternative earthing arrangements shall be made in consultation with the electricity supplier and in accordance with BS 7430.

4.2.6 Water temperatures

In other than single dwellings checks shall be made on the temperature of water in pipes, cold water cisterns, hot water storage vessels and the discharge from taps to ensure that they are within the limits as listed in **2.6.4**.

COMMENTARY AND RECOMMENDATIONS ON 4.2.6

These checks should be carried out during the most adverse conditions, such as at the end of a weekend, during hot weather, full central heating load in the case of cold weather and during high draw-off in cold conditions.

Should checks reveal unacceptable temperatures, it will be necessary to install additional insulation, trace heating or carry out modifications or repairs to the systems.

4.2.7 Cleaning and disinfection

Where there is a risk of legionella colonization of water services the system shall be cleaned and disinfected:

   a) if the system, or part of it, has been substantially altered or opened for maintenance purposes in a manner which may lead to contamination;

   b) following an outbreak or suspected outbreak of legionellosis.

COMMENTS AND RECOMMENDATIONS ON 4.2.7

Disinfection of the water system may be undertaken;

   a) for both the cold and hot water system, as described in 3.1.10; and

   b) for the hot water system only, by thermal disinfection procedures. (See HS(G)70 [3].)

© BSI 1997

4.3 Pipework

4.3.1 Fixings and supports

Provision for expansion and contraction shall be checked. Any loose or missing fixings or supports shall be replaced.

4.3.2 Joints

Leaking joints shall be rectified or where necessary the pipework shall be renewed, to stop all leakage.

4.3.3 Compatibility

When carrying out renewals, the existing pipework shall be identified and appropriate adaptors used, particularly where the original pipework is an imperial size.

COMMENTARY AND RECOMMENDATIONS ON 4.3.3

Pipes, fittings, components and materials of one manufacturer are not always compatible with those of another manufacturer, even when they conform to the same British Standard. This applies particularly to welding of plastics pipes, sockets for patent elastomeric ring joints and the threads on compression fittings.

4.3.4 Corrosion

If inspection of the system reveals leaks or leaks which have stifled, that component of the system shall be replaced and the offending parts examined by an expert to determine the cause of the leakage. Further action shall be dependent on the results of the examination and recommendations of the examining expert.

COMMENTARY AND RECOMMENDATIONS ON 4.3.4

Pipes showing signs of serious external corrosion should be replaced. The replacement pipe should have suitable protection (e.g. factory plastics coated, spirally wrapped or sleeved with an impervious material) or should be of a corrosion resistant material compatible with the remaining pipework.

4.3.5 Thermal insulation and fire stopping

Any damage to thermal insulation or fire stopping revealed during inspection shall be rectified.

COMMENTARY AND RECOMMENDATIONS ON 4.3.5

The integrity of thermal insulation used for frost protection should be checked at the beginning of winter.

4.4 Terminal fittings, valves and meters

Leakage from a float-operated valve (e.g. dripping from a warning pipe) or tap shall be rectified to stop the leakage. Self-closing taps shall be checked at regular intervals to ensure that the period of closing is not excessive.

COMMENTARY AND RECOMMENDATIONS ON 4.4

In addition to preventing leakage, the free movement of infrequently used float-operated valves, particularly those fitted to the feed and expansion cisterns of hot water or space heating systems should be checked at intervals not exceeding one year.

Spray heads on taps and showers should be cleaned periodically and descaled.

Gland packings on taps should be tightened or renewed as necessary to prevent any leakage while not impeding the normal operation of the fitting.

Stopvalves should be operated at least once per year to ensure free movement of working parts.

Any stiffness or leakage through the gland should be dealt with by lubrication, adjustment or replacement of gland packings or seals. If there is any indication of leakage past the seating the valve should be rewashered, reseated or replaced as necessary. If there is any indication that the waterway is blocked, the valve should be dismantled, cleared and restored to good working order or replaced.

Operation of easing gear may cause the valve to leak.

Meters (other than the water supplier's meters) should be removed at such intervals as experience shows necessary for cleaning and renewal of worn parts, and recalibration.

Any indication of malfunction of a pressure control valve should be investigated and remedied.

Discharge from an expansion valve or from a cistern warning pipe indicates a possible malfunction of a pressure reducing valve, pressure limiting valve or expansion vessel.

Where a pressure gauge is fitted downstream of a pressure control valve, its reading should be checked from time to time and any changes investigated.

4.5 Cisterns

Cisterns shall be inspected to ensure that overflow and warning pipes are clear, that covers are adequate and securely fixed, and that there are no signs of leakage or deterioration likely to result in leakage. Cisterns storing drinking water shall be inspected annually or more frequently if contamination is suspected.

COMMENTARY AND RECOMMENDATIONS ON 4.5

Cisterns are weak points in the prevention of contamination of water distribution systems and therefore require particular attention. Overflow and warning pipes should be checked from time to time to ensure that they conform to 2.2.4. All debris should be removed from cisterns and should be emptied, cleaned and disinfected. Where drinking water has been stored in an inadequately protected cistern, a water analysis should be considered (see 4.2.4) and adequate protection installed (see 2.2.3.1.1).

Metal cisterns showing signs of leakage or corrosion should preferably be replaced but they can be repaired by internal coating or lining, in accordance with the manufacturer's instructions, with a material conforming to BS 6920 as suitable for use in contact with drinking water.

In cistern installations, a check should be made for stagnant water. If stagnant water is found, the cistern(s) should be flushed and the flow configuration modified so that the flow displaces the whole of the contents continually when the cistern is in routine use.

4.6 Ducts

Ducts shall be kept accessible, clear of debris and free from vermin.

COMMENTARY AND RECOMMENDATIONS ON 4.6

All access points should be checked to ensure that they have not been obstructed. Regular inspections should be made to detect any vermin and any necessary measures taken for disinfestation.

Crawlways and subways should be inspected at intervals not exceeding 6 months. They should be checked for leakage from pipework, ingress of ground or surface water and accumulation of flammable materials.

4.7 Vessels under pressure

Any vessels storing water under pressure shall be inspected for indications of deterioration no less frequently than at the intervals recommended by the manufacturer.

Expansion vessels shall be inspected for indications of deterioration in strength and the gas pressure measured no less frequently than at the intervals recommended by the manufacturer. If the gas pressure is not within the limits specified for the application it shall be adjusted to within those limits.

4.8 Disconnection of unused pipes and fittings

If any part of an installation becomes redundant, and in particular if any appliance or fitting is disconnected, other than for the purpose of repair, maintenance or renewal, then the whole of the pipework supplying water to the disconnected or unused appliance or fitting shall also be disconnected at the source.

COMMENTARY AND RECOMMENDATIONS ON 4.8

It is undesirable and may be dangerous to have lengths of pipework containing motionless or stagnant water connected to the service installation. The water byelaws prescribe a maximum period of 60 days during which water fittings may be disconnected for repair or renewal without disconnecting the pipework supplying them with water.

© BSI 1997

Annexes

Annex A (informative)
Legal issues

A.1 Building regulations

A.1.1 *England and Wales*

The Building Regulations made by the Secretary of State for the Environment under the Building Act 1984 cover the health and safety of persons in and about buildings. Requirements are not included for the direct supply of public utilities, such as water, gas or electricity although (six) specified items are related to water installations.

The requirements for these items are made under regulations 4, 5 and 6 and listed in schedule 1 of the regulations to cover:

– provision of wash basins in conjunction with water closets and a suitable installation for the provision of hot and cold water to wash basins and provision for effective cleaning of water closets and urinals (G1);

– provision of a bath or shower bath and a suitable installation for the provision of hot and cold water to the bath or shower bath (G2);

– provision of sufficient precautions against explosion in unvented hot water systems (G3);

– requirements for controls on certain space and water heating installations and insulation of hot water heating and supply pipes, warm air ducts and hot water storage vessels (L1).

The requirements apply to the construction or installations work and there is no on-going requirement for maintenance or inspection. They are written in a functional form. The regulations are a statutory instrument; guidance on ways of meeting the requirements is given in approved documents.

Control of building work under the regulations is a matter for local authorities or approved inspectors. Local authorities also have powers under other sanitation and building legislation such as the Public Health Acts. Local authorities and approved inspectors also have powers to inspect work during construction. Disputes regarding a local authority's application of the regulations may have to be decided ultimately in a court of law; it is not always appreciated that contravening building regulations is a criminal offence.

Building work generally involves more than one statutory instrument and any person undertaking water installations or other works should be aware of the relevant requirements in such statutory or guidance documents as building regulations, water byelaws, gas regulations and electrical wiring regulations.

A.1.2 *Scotland*

In Scotland the Building Standards (Scotland) Regulations, made under the Building (Scotland) Act 1959, apply in respect of:

– drainage and sanitary facilities (M);

– requirements for unvented hot water systems (P);

– insulation of hot water storage vessels and pipes (J).

A.1.3 *Northern Ireland*

In Northern Ireland the Building (Northern Ireland) Regulations, made under the Building Regulations (Northern Ireland) Order 1979, apply in respect of:

– drainage and sanitary facilities (N);

– unvented hot water systems (P);

– conservation of fuel and power (F).

A.2 Water regulations and water byelaws

A.2.1 *England and Wales*

In England and Wales, the law on the provision of water supply is now prescribed in the Water Industry Act 1991. The act provides for the Secretary of State for the Environment to make regulations for preventing contamination, waste and undue consumption of water supplied by water suppliers. Until such regulations are made, the water byelaws made by the undertakers and which came into effect on 1 January 1989, will continue to apply.

Building owners or occupiers can demand a supply of water for domestic purposes provided they have complied with the relevant requirements of The Water Industry Act 1991 and the installation satisfies the requirements of water byelaws.

If any water supplier considers that the enforcement of any byelaw would be unreasonable in relation to a particular case, an application should be made to the Secretary of State for the Environment for a relaxation of that byelaw. It is advisable to consult the water supplier at an early stage, not only regarding water byelaw matters in general, but also as regards any particular requirements of byelaws arising from any local soil or water characteristic.

Although the installation of a new water service, or repairs or extensions to any existing service, are not, as yet required to be undertaken by suitably qualified persons, whoever undertakes the work may be liable to any penalties imposed by the courts for contravention of any of the water byelaws. It should also be noted that the use of any fitting which can be said to violate the water byelaws may also constitute an offence. In these cases the householder would be liable to prosecution on conviction. An adequate knowledge of the water byelaws is, therefore, most desirable not only for installers but also for the user.

Water supplies for non-domestic services will need to be negotiated with individual water suppliers (see section 27 Water Act 1945 for England and Wales). See also section 60 Schedule III Water Act 1945 in respect of secondary backflow protection related to intermittent supplies.

A.2.2 *Scotland*

In Scotland, water byelaws are made under section 70 of the Water (Scotland) Act 1980. The arrangements in Scotland are similar to those in England and Wales except that the water authorities are the water undertakers. However, there are differences in detail between the byelaws operating in Scotland and those operating in England and Wales.

The Building Standards (Scotland) Regulations require an adequate supply of water available within the house. The majority of other types of buildings are required to have a water supply for sanitary purposes.

A.2.3 *Northern Ireland*

In Northern Ireland, water regulations have been made under Article 40 of the Water and Sewerage Services (Northern Ireland) Order 1973. The general purpose is to prohibit the use or connection of fittings that are likely to cause or permit waste, undue consumption, misuse, erroneous measurement or contamination of water supplied by the Department of the Environment for Northern Ireland.

A.3 The New Roads and Street Works Act 1991

This Act amends existing legislation relating to and enabling the provision of new roads and makes provisions in respect of street works and connected purposes.

A.4 The Health and Safety at Work etc. Act 1974

This act makes provisions for securing the health, safety and welfare of persons at work, for controlling the keeping and use of dangerous substances and for controlling certain emissions into the atmosphere. The Workplace (Health, Safety and Welfare) Regulations are made under this act and regulate the provision of drinking water and sanitary accommodation at places of work. The Gas Safety (Installation and Use) Regulations regulate the installation of gas appliances and systems. The provision and method of using asbestos containing materials is covered by the Control of Asbestos at Work Regulations which are made under this act.

Annex B (informative)
Examples of pumped systems

B.1 Introduction

There are many ways of using pumps to increase the water pressure available in a building. These can be divided into direct boosting and indirect boosting systems. Indirect systems are more common than direct systems; the latter are often prohibited by water suppliers because they reduce the mains pressure available to other consumers and can increase the risk of backflow.

Booster pumps can cause excessive aeration: although this does not cause deterioration of water quality, the turbid appearance of aerated water can cause concern amongst consumers.

The provision of sampling taps on outlets from booster pumps is desirable.

The following systems are given as examples:

    a) indirect boosting to storage cistern;

    b) indirect boosting with pressure vessel;

    c) direct boosting;

    d) direct boosting to header and duplicate storage cisterns.

B.2 Indirect boosting to storage cistern

Where the water supplier insists on a break cistern being incorporated in the installation, the pumps should be fitted to the outlet from the break cistern. The effective capacity of the break cistern should be decided after consideration of the total water storage requirements and its location within the building, but should be not less than 15 min of pump output. The cistern should not be oversized as this could result in stagnation of the water.

The water level in the storage cistern or cisterns is controlled by means of water level switches controlling the pumps. When the water level drops to a predetermined value, the pumps start and are switched off when the water level reaches a point approximately 50 mm below the float-operated valve shut-off level. Additionally, a water level switch should be positioned in the break cistern to cut out the pumps when the level of water in the break cistern drops to approximately 225 mm above the pump suction connection. This will ensure that the pumps do not run dry. (See figure B.1.)

© BSI 1997

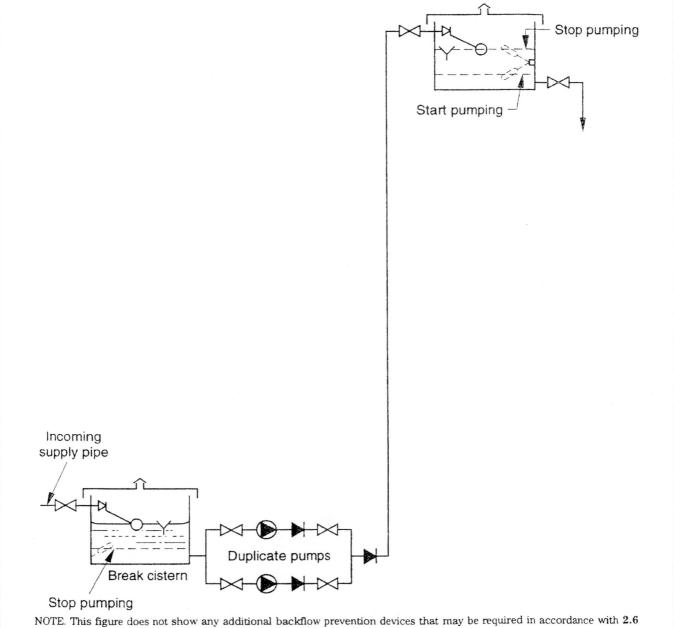

Stop pumping

Start pumping

Incoming
supply pipe

Duplicate pumps

Break cistern

Stop pumping

NOTE. This figure does not show any additional backflow prevention devices that may be required in accordance with **2.6**

Figure B.1 Indirect boosting from break cistern to storage cistern

B.3 Indirect boosting with pressure vessel

In buildings where a boosted supply serves a number of delivery points or storage cisterns at various levels, e.g. in flats, it may not be practicable to control the pumps by means of a number of level switches.

An alternative method of control is by use of a pneumatic pressure vessel which contains both air and water under pressure (see figure B.2). Normally the pressure vessel, pumps and air compressor, together with all control equipment are purchased as a packaged pressure set.

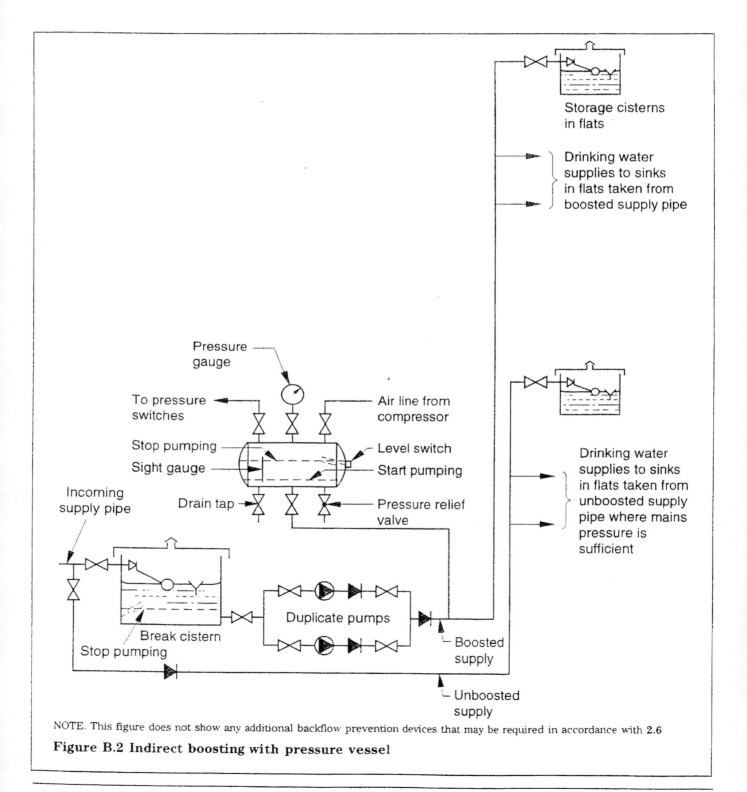

NOTE. This figure does not show any additional backflow prevention devices that may be required in accordance with 2.6

Figure B.2 Indirect boosting with pressure vessel

B.4 Direct boosting

Where the water supplier has given prior written permission, pumps are connected to the incoming supply pipe to enable the pressure head to be increased (see figure B.3).

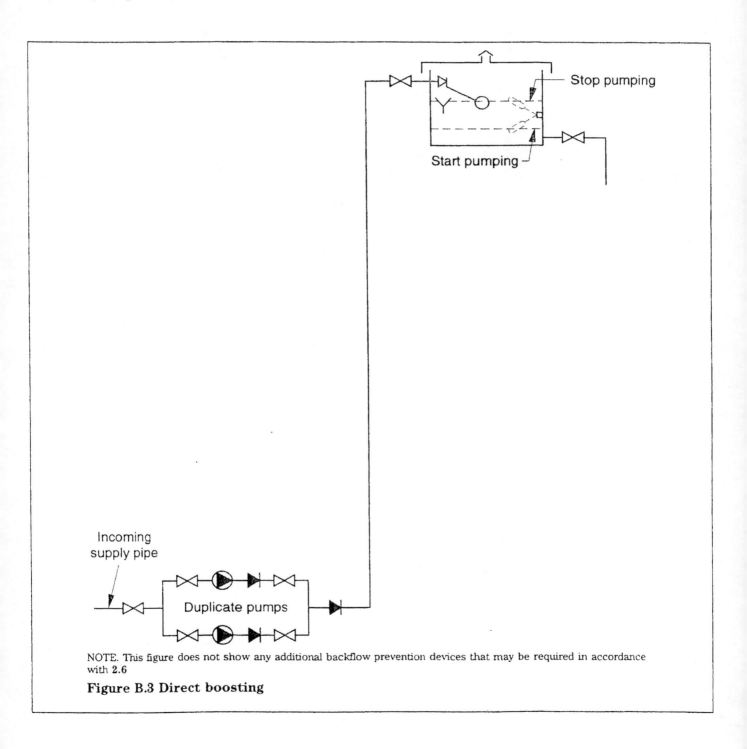

NOTE. This figure does not show any additional backflow prevention devices that may be required in accordance with **2.6**

Figure B.3 Direct boosting

B.5 Direct boosting with drinking water header

The provision of supply drinking water points at high level when the pump is not running, where required, may be achieved by a pipe arrangement of limited capacity called a header (see figure B.4). Level switches should be provided to control the filling of the cold water storage cisterns for non-drinking water. Excessive pressures should not be generated, since high pressures at draw-off points cause splashing and waste of water when taps are opened. The boosting pumps are controlled in two ways:

a) by the emptying of, or drop in level of, the water in the header; and

b) by the fall of the level of water in one of the storage cisterns.

The cold water main header should be sized on the basis of providing 5 l to 7 l per day per dwelling served and the rising pipe from the header should be provided with an automatic air inlet valve to allow air to enter and be vented from the header.

B.6 Pumps and equipment

Electrically-driven centrifugal pumping plant is normally used. Where prudent, provision should be made for the pumps to be supplied by an alternative electricity supply in the event of mains failure.

Pumps should be installed in duplicate and used alternately. They should be sized so that each pump is capable of overcoming the static lift plus the friction losses in the pipework and valves. All pipework connections to and from pumps should be adequately supported and anchored against thrust to avoid stress on pump casings and to ensure proper alignment.

Transmission of pump and motor noise can be reduced by the use of flexible connections and anti-vibration mountings or pads. Small-power motors of the squirrel cage induction type are suitable for most installations. Care should be taken in pump and pipe sizing to minimize the risk of water-hammer due to surge when pumps are started and stopped.

B.7 Maintenance and inspection

A responsible person should oversee the proper execution of the scheme and the user should arrange for regular maintenance and inspection of the pumps and plant.

All work conducted and inspections made should be recorded in a suitable log book which should be kept in the plant room

COMMENTARY AND RECOMMENDATIONS ON B.7

Attention is drawn to to Health and Safety at Work Act 1974 with respect to the inspection of pumps and plant.

© BSI 1997

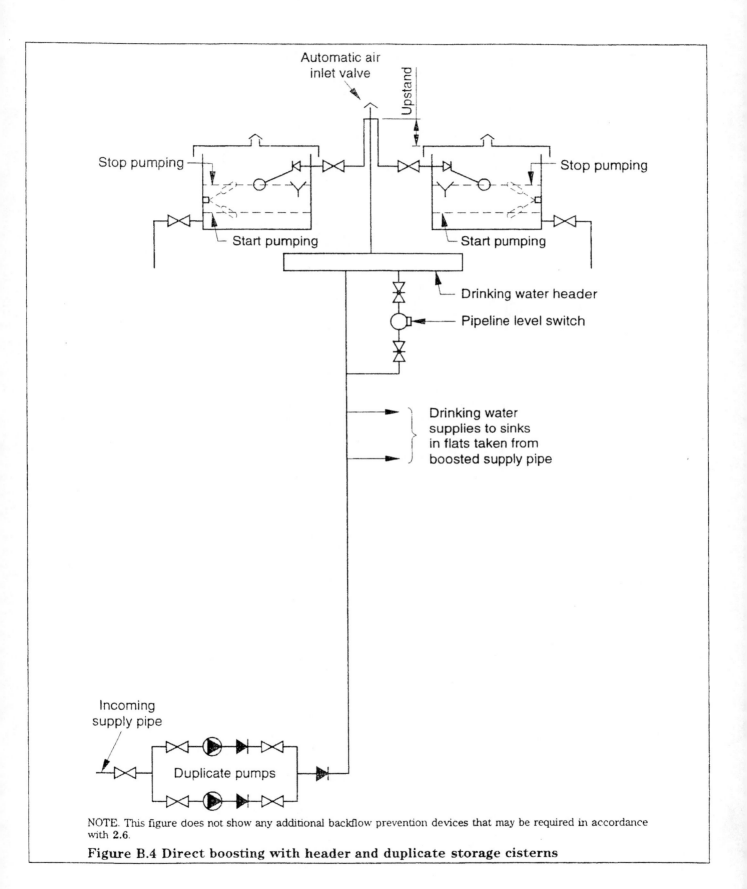

NOTE. This figure does not show any additional backflow prevention devices that may be required in accordance with **2.6**.

Figure B.4 Direct boosting with header and duplicate storage cisterns

Annex C (informative)

Guidance on the calculation of hot water storage capacity

The storage capacity required to achieve an acceptable quality of service depends upon the rate of heat input to the stored hot water as well as on the pattern of use. The time M (in min) taken to heat a quantity of water through a specified temperature rise is given by:

$$M = VT/(14.3P)$$

where

V is the volume of water heated (in l);

T is the temperature rise (in K);

P is the rate of heat input to water (in kW).

This formula ignores heat losses from the hot water storage vessel, since over the relatively short times involved in reheating water after a draw-off has taken place their effect is usually small.

For an electric immersion heater, a directly gas-fired storage water heater and a direct boiler system, the value of P is the output of the heating appliance. For an indirect boiler system, the value of P will depend upon the temperature of the stored water, since heat will pass from the primary circuit to the secondary circuit at a faster rate when the secondary water is cold than when it is hot. For practical purposes a simple approximation by taking an average value for P will usually suffice. An indirect cylinder conforming to BS 1566 : Part 1 will accept heat inputs up to about 15 kW, with pumped primary flow.

Typical values for P are:

– 3 kW for an electric immersion heater;

– 3 kW for a gas-fired circulator;

– 6 kW for a small boiler and direct cylinder;

– 10 kW for a medium boiler and indirect cylinder;

– 10 kW for a directly gas-fired storage water heater (domestic type);

– 15 kW for a large domestic boiler and indirect cylinder.

The application of this formula to the sizing of hot water cylinders is best illustrated by the following examples, in which figures have been rounded.

Examples of application

Case 1. Small dwelling with one bath installed.

Maximum requirement: one bath (60 l at 60 °C plus 40 l cold water) plus 10 l hot water at 60 °C for kitchen use followed by a second bath fill after 25 min.

Thus draw-off of 70 l at 60 °C followed after 25 min by 100 l at 40 °C is required, which may be achieved by mixing hot at 60 °C with cold at 10 °C.

Firstly assume good stratification, e.g. heating by the top-entry immersion heater.

To heat 60 l from 10 °C to 60 °C using a 3 kW input takes $(60 \times 50) / (14.3 \times 3) = 70$ min so the second bath has to be provided from storage. In 25 min the volume of water heated to 60 °C is $14.3 \times 3 \times 25 \div 50 = 21$ l.

Therefore the minimum storage capacity to meet requirement is $70 + 60 - 21 = 109$ l.

To heat 60 l from 10 °C to 60 °C using a 6 kW input takes $(60 \times 50) / (14.3 \times 6) = 35$ min so, again, the second bath has to be provided from storage.

In 25 min the volume of water heated from 10 °C to 60 °C is $14.3 \times 6 \times 25 \div 50 = 42$ l. Hence the minimum storage capacity to meet the requirement is $70 + 60 - 42 = 88$ l. To heat 60 l from 10 °C to 60 °C using 10 kW input takes $(60 \times 50)/(14.3 \times 10) = 21$ min so the second bath requires no storage and minimum storage requirement is that to provide bath plus kitchen use, i.e. 70 l.

With 15 kW input of heat to the water the storage volume could be reduced to 60 l since while the first bath is running, taking about 3 min, the heat input to the water is sufficient to raise about 11 l water from 10 °C to 60 °C, so providing for kitchen use. This could be negated by mixing, and is not recommended for this duty.

Now assuming good mixing of the stored water, as would occur with heating by a primary coil in an indirect cylinder, the temperature of the stored water immediately after the 70 l draw-off would be $\{(V - 70) \times 60 + 70 \times 10\} \div V$, which simplifies to $60 - 3500/V$. The formula shows that heating for 25 min at 3 kW will raise the temperature through $3 \times 25 \times 14.3/V$ or $1072.5/V$.

Since a water temperature of at least 40 °C is required to run a second bath:

$$(60 - 3500/V) + (1072.5/V) = 40 \text{ (or more)}$$

where

$V = 122$ l

Using 6 kW heat input the temperature rise in 25 min is $2145/V$ which gives a minimum size of 68 l. This, however, would not meet the requirement of 100 l at 40 °C for a bath. In fact, a vessel of 88 l capacity, which would attain a temperature of about 44.5 °C after 25 min would just suffice, but for simplicity a cylinder of about 100 l capacity would normally be chosen.

For heat inputs of 10 kW and 15 kW a 70 l hot water storage vessel is required as before, the need to draw-off for bath and kitchen use dictating the minimum storage capacity.

Thus for case 1, the minimum sizes of storage vessel are given in table C.1.

Table C.1 Minimum sizes of storage vessel for case 1

Heat input to water	Minimum storage capacity l	
kW	With stratification	With mixing
3	109	122
6	88	88
10	70	70
15	70	70

Case 2. A dwelling with two baths installed and having a maximum requirement of 130 l drawn off at 60 °C (2 baths + 10 l for kitchen use) followed by a further bath (100 l at 40 °C) after 30 min.

The calculations follow the same procedures as for case 1 and the results for case 2 are given in table C.2.

Table C.2 Minimum sizes of storage vessel for case 2

Heat input to water	Minimum storage capacity l	
kW	With stratification	With mixing
3	165	260
6	140	200
10	130	130
15	120	130

These calculations, which may be carried out for any particular situation, indicate the value of promoting stratification wherever possible and show the order of savings in storage capacity that can be made without prejudice to the quality of the service to the user by increasing the heat input to the water.

Annex D (informative)
Pipe sizing calculations

D.1 Determination of flow rates

D.1.1 *General*

In small, simple installations such as those in single dwellings, it is often acceptable to size pipes on the basis of experience and convention. In all other cases the probable flow rates and pipe sizes required should be calculated using a recognized method of calculation, such as the method given in this annex.

D.1.2 *Assessment of probable demand*

In most buildings all appliances are seldom in simultaneous use. For reasons of economy a simultaneous demand which is less than the maximum demand from all appliances should be provided for. This simultaneous demand can be estimated either from data derived by observation and experience of similar installations, or by application of probability theory using loading units.

D.1.3 *Loading units (LU)*

Loading units are factors which take into account the flow rate at the appliance, the length of time in use and the frequency of use. The number of each type of appliance, fed by the length of pipe being considered, should be multiplied by the loading units, as given in table D.1, and the total LU derived for the pipe. Using figure D.1 the total number of LU can be converted into the total simultaneous demand for the pipe in l/s. Owing to the difference in rates of flow and pattern of demand between hot and cold outlets, the LU applicable also show some variation, but for most practical purposes the same LUs can be used for both hot and cold outlets.

Table D.1 is based on normal domestic usage and customary (or statutory) provision of appliances. It is not applicable where usage is intensive, for example, in theatres and conference halls; in such cases it is necessary to establish the pattern of usage and appropriate peak flow demand for the particular case.

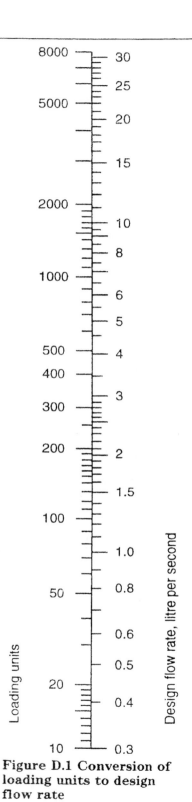

Figure D.1 Conversion of loading units to design flow rate

Table D.1 Loading units (hot or cold supply)	
Type of appliance	Loading units
WC flushing cistern	2
Wash basin $\frac{1}{2}$ - DN 15	1.5 to 3
Bath tap $\frac{3}{4}$ - DN 20	10
Bath tap 1 - DN 25	22
Shower	3
Sink tap $\frac{1}{2}$ - DN 15	3
Sink tap $\frac{3}{4}$ - DN 20	5
Domestic clothes or dishwashing machines $\frac{1}{2}$ - DN 15	3

NOTE 1. WC cisterns with either single or dual flush control have the same LU.

NOTE 2. The wash basin LU is for use where pillar taps are installed. The larger LU is applicable to situations such as schools and those offices where there is a peak period of use. Where spray taps are installed, an equivalent continuous demand of 0.04 l/s should be assumed.

NOTE 3. Urinal cistern demand is very low, and is normally disregarded.

NOTE 4. Outlet fittings for industrial purposes or requiring high peak demands, should be taken into account by adding 100 % of their flow rate to the simultaneous demand for other appliances obtained by using LUs.

D.2 Pressure losses in pipes and fittings

D.2.1 *Pipes and pipe fittings*

Pressure, or head, losses due to resistance of pipes and fittings at various flows are published in the form of tables for pipes of different materials by the various pipe manufacturers organizations. A nomogram showing pressure losses and flows of water at a temperature of 10 °C through pipes, based on Lamont's smooth pipe formula S3, is shown in figure D.2.

Typical values for equivalent pipe lengths for elbows and tees are shown in table D.3.

D.2.2 *Draw-off taps*

The residual head available at each tap or outlet fitting should be at least equal to the loss of head through the tap at the design flow rate. Alternatively, the loss of head may be expressed as an equivalent length of pipe. Some typical losses for low pressure taps are shown in table D.2.

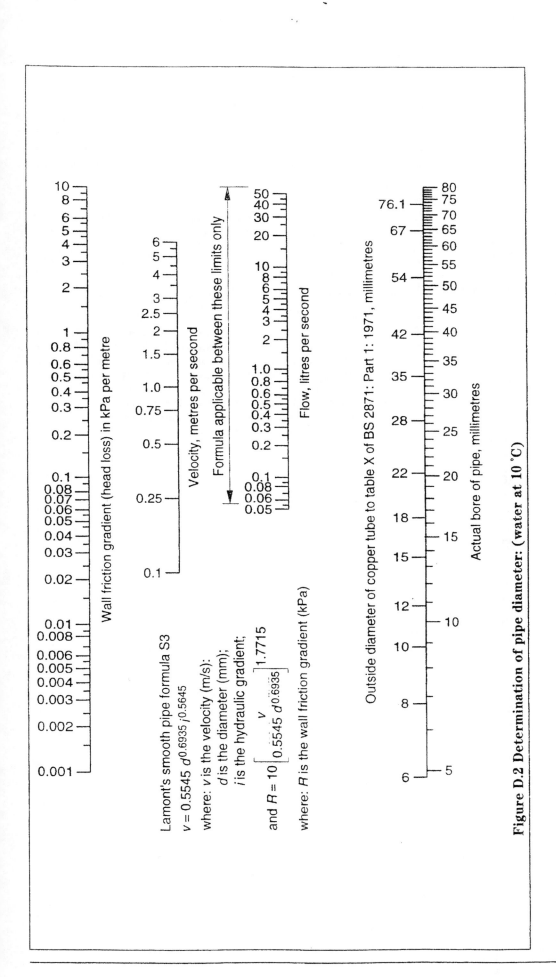

Figure D.2 Determination of pipe diameter: (water at 10 °C)

Table D.2 Typical loss of pressure through UK low resistance taps and equivalent pipe lengths

Nominal size of tap	Flow rate	Loss of pressure	Equivalent pipe length
	l/s	kPa	m
$\frac{1}{2}$	0.15	5	3.7
$\frac{1}{2}$	0.20	8	3.7
$\frac{3}{4}$	0.30	8	11.8
1	0.60	15	22.0

NOTE. Pressure losses and equivalent lengths are typical only and will vary with taps of different manufacture.

Table D.3 Typical equivalent pipe lengths (copper, plastics and stainless steel)

Bore of pipe	Equivalent pipe length			
	Elbow	Tee	Stop valve	Check valve
mm	m	m	m	m
12	0.5	0.6	4.0	2.5
20	0.8	1.0	7.0	4.3
25	1.0	1.5	10.0	5.6
32	1.4	2.0	13.0	6.0
40	1.7	2.5	16.0	7.9
50	2.3	3.5	22.0	11.5
65	3.0	4.5	—	—
73	3.4	5.8	34.0	—

NOTE 1. The losses through tees are taken to occur on a change of direction only. Losses through fully open gate valves may be ignored.

NOTE 2. In some systems special fittings and significant head losses are used. For information on head losses in these fittings, reference should be made to the manufacturers.

D.2.3 *Valves*

The loss of head through stopvalves and check valves is relatively large. These losses are expressed either as the loss of head through an equivalent length of pipe as in table D.3 and added to the actual length, or the actual head loss determined from figure D.3 and subtracted from the head available. The losses through full way gate valves can be ignored.

D.2.4 *Meters*

If there is a meter in the pipeline, the loss of head through the meter at design flow should be deducted from the available head. The loss of head at specific flows can be obtained from the meter manufacturer or from the water supplier.

D.2.5 *Float-operated valves*

The nominal size of a float-operated valve, the diameter of its orifice and the size of the float are all dependent on the residual head of water available at the inlet to the valve and the flow required. The relationship between discharge, size of valve, orifice and head loss is shown in figure D.4. Where non-standard float valves are used, the data relating the flow rate to the head of water available at the inlet should be obtained from the manufacturer.

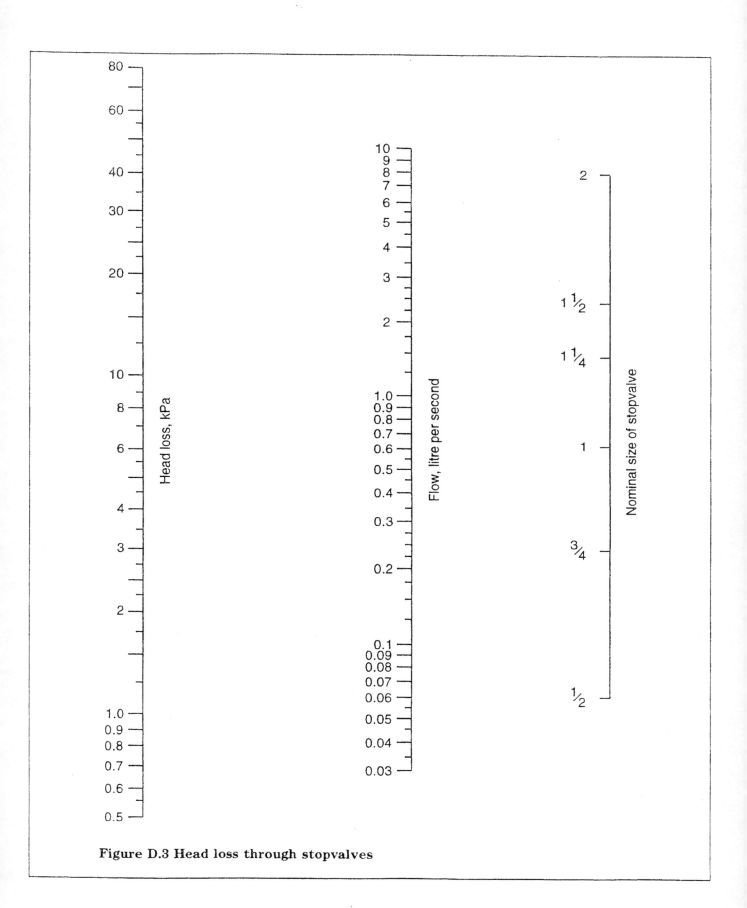

Figure D.3 Head loss through stopvalves

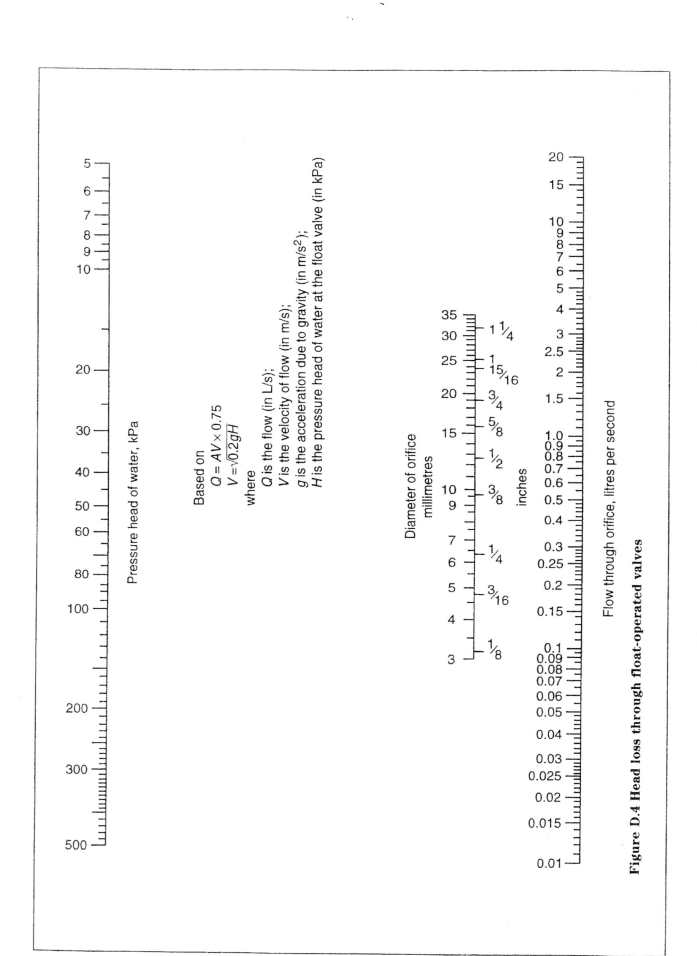

Based on

$Q = AV \times 0.75$

$V = \sqrt{0.2gH}$

where

Q is the flow (in L/s);

V is the velocity of flow (in m/s);

g is the acceleration due to gravity (in m/s^2);

H is the pressure head of water at the float valve (in kPa)

Pressure head of water, kPa

Diameter of orifice millimetres

inches

Flow through orifice, litres per second

Figure D.4 Head loss through float-operated valves

D.3 Available head

D.3.1 *Systems supplied from storage cisterns*

The initial available head should normally be measured from the outlet of a cistern, unless the incoming supply is sufficient to allow a depth of half the cistern or 0.5 m, whichever is less to be assumed. Each pipe length between pipe junctions should be sized on a trial and error basis, starting with the first length of pipe from the cistern. The residual head at the end of each pipe length should be calculated taking account of head losses in pipework, fittings and valves. If a residual head is arrived at that is negative or less than the head absorbed by the outlet or tap, of if an impractical pipe size is indicated, the diameter of the preceding pipes should be adjusted and the procedure repeated.

D.3.2 *Systems supplied from the supply pipe (mains pressure)*

The minimum pressure in the main at the time of peak demand should be obtained from the water supplier and if there is any doubt about the pressure being obtainable in the future a suitable factor should be applied. Once the minimum pressure has been established the method for pipe sizing is identical with that indicated in **D.4.1**.

D.4 Determination of pipe sizes

D.4.1 *General*

The principle underlying design of a water supply system is the same whether cold and hot water supplies to appliances are obtained from a storage cistern or direct from a main service pipe. Friction losses in the pipes may be determined by the general theory or roughness, but this has too many variables for normal design purposes. Exponential formulae have been devised, which relate pipe diameter to head loss, water velocity and flow for new pipes in smooth-bore materials. Reduction in capacity with age can be ignored for pipe sizing calculations for pipes carrying clean portable water within buildings. Using flow charts which are based on exponential formulae, a pipe diameter can be selected which meets the other three design parameters of design flow, maximum water velocity and permissible head loss.

D.4.2 *Calculation diagrams*

An approximate isometric or similar projection of the scheme should be drawn. This drawing should be to scale to facilitate measurement of pipe lengths and levels unless the data can be obtained otherwise. The possibility of future extensions or additions to the scheme should be considered at this stage. Each pipe junction and fitting should be numbered for calculation purposes and pipes referenced by their terminal junctions and fittings.

D.4.3 *Calculation sheet*

A calculation sheet should be used on which the following data can be entered (see attached calculation sheets **D.4** and **D.5**):

    a) pipe reference;

    b) total demand in loading units (LU);

    c) simultaneous demand or design flow rate (in l/s);

    d) pipe diameter (in mm);

    e) velocity (in m/s);

    f) head or pressure loss R (in kPa/m);

    g) loss of head (in kPa) due to drop or rise, that is, the difference in level of inlet and outlet;

    h) available head (in kPa) at outlet end of pipe length;

    i) actual pipe length (in m);

    j) equivalent pipe length (in m), that is, the actual plus an allowance for fittings;

    k) head loss (in kPa) due to pipe and pipe fittings;

    l) head loss (in kPa) due to valves etc.;

    m) total head loss (in kPa);

    n) available residual head (in kPa) at outlet of pipe length;

    o) appliance or fitting type (bath, sink, etc.);

    p) required residual head for fitting (in kPa);

    q) surplus head (in kPa).

D.4.4 *Alterations and extensions*

Where an extension or alteration is carried out to old pipework, the existing pipes may be of imperial sizes, and the calculations should be adjusted accordingly.

D.4.5 *Examples of calculation procedure*

Example calculations for determining the sizes of pipes for a cold and hot water system installed in flats in a three-storey building are given below for:

Example 1. Low pressure system; most appliances supplied from storage cistern. See pipe diagram shown in figure D.5 and calculation sheets given in table D.4.

Example 2. All appliances served from supply pipe under mains pressure. See pipe diagram shown in figure D.6 and calculation sheets given in table D.5.

Stage	Procedure	Complete column
1.	Prepare the pipework diagram and number each junction consecutively from the cistern or water main.	
2.	Enter the pipe reference on the calculation sheet.	1.
3.	Determine the loading units for each length of pipe from table D.1.	2.
4.	Convert the loading units to design flow rates in l/s using figure D.1.	3.
5.	Starting from the source and using a straightedge in conjunction with figure D.2, select a pipe size, such that the velocity is 3 m/s or less. Note the velocity and pressure loss per metre of pipe.	4, 5 and 6.
6.	Determine the pressure difference due to the vertical distance between the inlet and the outlet of the pipe length (+ drop or − rise).	7.

Stage	Procedure	Complete column
7.	Determine the available head by adding or deducting the pressure difference due to the drop or rise respectively to or from the residual head available at the inlet to the pipe length.	8.
8.	Measure the actual length of the pipe being considered.	9.
9.	Determine the effective length of the pipe by adding on to the actual length an equivalent length of pipe to allow for pressure losses in pipe fittings.	10.
10.	Determine the actual head loss of the pipework from the product of columns 6 and 10.	11.
11.	Determine the loss of pressure due to valves from table D.3.	12.
12.	Add columns 11 and 12 to determine the total head loss.	13.
13.	Deduct the actual head loss in column 13 from the available head in column 8 to give the residual head available.	14.
14.	If residual head is less than the head required for a particular outlet fitting (column 16), select a larger pipe size and repeat stages 5 to 14.	

© BSI 1997

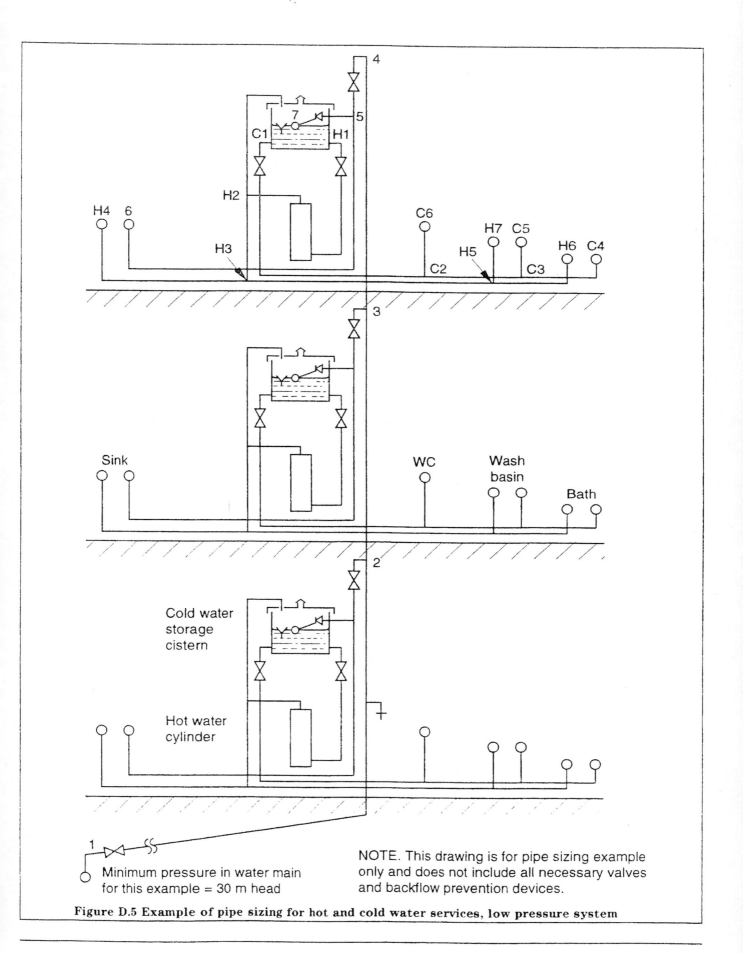

Minimum pressure in water main
for this example = 30 m head

NOTE. This drawing is for pipe sizing example
only and does not include all necessary valves
and backflow prevention devices.

Figure D.5 Example of pipe sizing for hot and cold water services, low pressure system

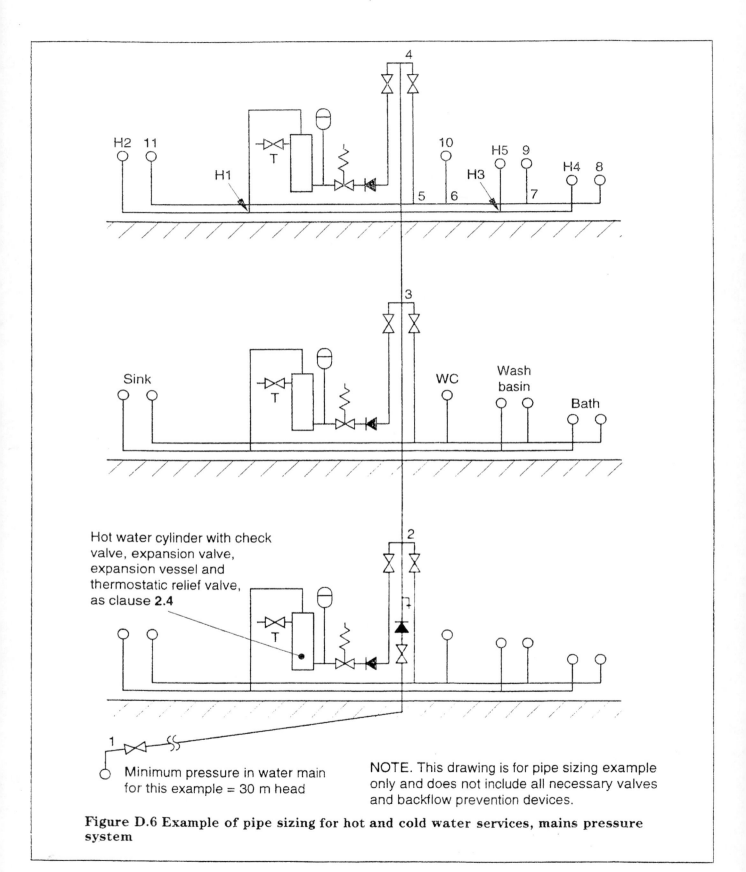

Figure D.6 Example of pipe sizing for hot and cold water services, mains pressure system

© BSI 1997

Table D.4 Example of pipe sizing calculations for cold water services[1]

Pipe reference	Flow rate Total	Flow rate Design	Pipe size	Velocity v	Head loss R	Drop + Rise −	Available head (7 + 14)	Pipe length Actual	Pipe length Effective	Head loss Pipe (10 × 6)	Head loss Valves[2]	Head loss Total (11 + 12)	Residual head Available (8 − 13)	Residual head Fitting type	Residual head Required	Residual head Surplus
m	LU	l/s	DN	m/s	kPa/m	kPa	kPa	m	m	kPa	kPa	kPa	kPa		kPa	kPa
1	2	3	4	5	6	7	8	9	10	11	12	13	14	15	16	17
Main service pipe - for this example the minimum head in main = 300 kPa (3 bar)																
1 – 2	9 + list	0.6 + 0.3 = 0.9	28	1.7	1.4	− 50	250	25	35	49	2 SV = 21	70	180			
2 – 3	6 + list	0.4 + 0.2 = 0.6	22	2.0	2.5	− 30	150	3	4.2	11		11	139			
3 – 4	3 + list	0.2 + 0.1 = 0.3	15	2.2	5	− 30	109	3	4.2	21		21	88			
4 – 5	3 + list	0.3	15	2.2	5	+ 10	98	1	1.4	7	SV = 18	25	73			
5 – 6		0.2	15	1.5	2.3	+ 10	83	6	8.4	20		20	63	sink	5	58
5 – 7		0.1	15	0.75	0.6	− 5	68	1	1.4	1		1	67	float valve (5 mm φ)	30	37
Cold water distributing pipes in flats																
C1 – C2	13.5	0.35	28	0.63	0.25	+20	20	4	5.6	1.4	Gate valve = 0	1.4	18.6			
C2 – C3	11.5	0.32	22	1	0.8	—	18.6	1	1.4	1.2		1.2	17.4			
C3 – C4	10.0	0.30	22	0.9	0.65	− 6	11.4	1.5	2.1	1.4		1.4	10	bath	8	2
C3 – C5	1.5	0.15	15	1.1	1.3	− 7	10.4	0.7	1.0	1.3		1.3	9.1	wash basin	8	1.1
C2 – C6	2.0	0.10	15	0.7	0.6	− 7	11.6	1	1.4	0.9		0.9	10.7	WC cistern (6.5 mm φ)	10	0.7

Table D.4 Example of pipe sizing calculations for cold water services[1] *(continued)*

Pipe reference	Flow rate		Pipe size	Velocity	Head loss R	Drop + Rise −	Available head (7 + 14)	Pipe length		Head loss			Residual head			
	Total	Design		v				Actual	Effective	Pipe (10 × 6)	Valves[2]	Total (11 + 12)	Available (8 − 13)	Fitting type	Required	Surplus
m	LU	l/s	DN	m/s	kPa/m	kPa	kPa	m	m	kPa	kPa	kPa	kPa		kPa	kPa
1	2	3	4	5	6	7	8	9	10	11	12	13	14	15	16	17
Hot water distributing pipes in flats																
H1 – H2	14.5	0.37	28	0.75	0.3	+ 10	10	4.0	5.6	1.7	Gate valve = 0	1.7	8.3			
H2 – H3	14.5	0.37	28	0.75	0.3	+ 10	18.3	1.5	2.1	0.6		0.6	17.7			
H3 – H4	3.0	0.20	22	0.65	0.31	− 10	7.7	3.0	4.2	1.3		1.3	6.4	sink	5	1.4
H3 – H5	11.5	0.32	28	0.65	0.24		17.7	3.0	4.2	1.0		1.0	16.7			
H5 – H6	10.0	0.30	22	0.9	0.65	− 6	10.7	1.5	2.1	1.4		1.4	9.3	bath	8	1.3
H5 – H7	1.5	0.15	15	1.1	1.3	− 7	9.7	0.7	1.0	1.3		1.3	8.4	wash basin	5	3.4

Charts used based on figure A.2.5 (water at 10 °C)

[1] Cistern supply-except for DW at sink

[2] SV = stopvalve   CV = check valve   DCV = Double check valve

1 kPa = 0.1 metre head = 0.01 bar

© BSI 1997

Table D.5 Example of pipe sizing calculations for cold water services (mains supplied)[1]

Pipe reference	Flow rate Total	Flow rate Design	Pipe size	Velocity v	Head loss R	Drop + Rise -	Available head (7 + 14)	Pipe length Actual	Pipe length Effective	Head loss Pipe (10 × 6)	Head loss Valves[1]	Head loss Total (11 + 12)	Residual head Available (8 – 13)	Residual head Fitting type	Residual head Required	Residual head Surplus
m	LU	l/s	DN	m/s	kPa/m	kPa	kPa	m	m	kPa	kPa	kPa	kPa		kPa	kPa
1	2	3	4	5	6	7	8	9	10	11	12	13	14	15	16	17
Supply pipes to flats - for this example the minimum head in main = 300 kPa (3 bar)														All calculations based on water at 10 °C		
1 – 2	93	1.17	28	2.3	2.1	– 40	260	24	33.6	71	2 SV +CV = 54	125	135			
2 – 3	62	0.90	28	1.7	1.4	– 30	105	3	4.2	6		6	99			
3 – 4	31	0.57	22	1.8	2.0	– 30	69	3	4.2	9		9	60			
Cold water services to top flat																
4 – 5	16.5	0.40	22	1.3	1.2	+ 20	80	2	2.8	4	SV = 8	12	68			
5 – 6	13.5	0.35	15	2.6	6.0		68	1	1.4	9		9	59			
6 – 7	11.5	0.32	15	2.3	5.2	– 5	59	1	1.4	8		8	51			
7 – 8	10.0	0.30	15	2.2	5.0	– 5	46	1.5	2.1	11		11	35	bath	8	27
7 – 9	1.5	0.15	15	1.1	1.4	– 7	44	0.7	1.0	2		2	42	wash basin	5	37
6 – 10	2.0	0.10	15	0.7	0.6	– 10	49	1	1.4	1		1	48	wc cistern	25 (5 mm)	23
5 – 11	3.0	0.20	15	1.5	2.3	– 10	58	4	5.6	13		13	45	sink	5	40

© BSI 1997

Table D.5 Example of pipe sizing calculations for cold water services (mains supplied)[1]

Pipe reference	Flow rate		Pipe size	Velocity	Head loss R	Drop + Rise -	Available head (7 + 14)	Pipe length		Head loss			Residual head			
	Total	Design		v				Actual	Effective	Pipe (10 × 6)	Valves[1]	Total (11 + 12)	Available (8 − 13)	Fitting type	Required	Surplus
m	LU	l/s	DN	m/s	kPa/m	kPa	kPa	m	m	kPa	kPa	kPa	kPa		kPa	kPa
1	2	3	4	5	6	7	8	9	10	11	12	13	14	15	16	17
Hot water supply to top flat (charts used based on water at 10 °C)																
4 – H1	14.5	0.37	22	1.1	0.9	+ 20	80	5.5	7.7	7	3 valves = 20	27	53			
H1 – H2	3.0	0.20	15	1.5	1.7	– 10	43	3	4.2	7		7	36	sink	5	31
H1 – H3	11.5	0.32	22	1.0	0.8		53	3	4.2	4		4	49			
H3 – H4	10.0	0.30	22	1.0	0.7	– 5	44	1.5	2.1	2		2	42	bath	8	34
H3 – H5	1.5	0.15	15	1.1	1.4	– 7	42	0.7	1.0	2		2	40	wash basin	5	35

1) SV = stopvalve   CV = check valve   DCV = Double check valve   1 kPa = 0.1 metre head = 0.01 bar

© BSI 1997

List of references (see 1.2)

Normative references

BSI publications

BRITISH STANDARDS INSTITUTION, London

BS 417 :	*Specification for galvanized low carbon steel cisterns, cistern lids, tanks and cylinders*
BS 417 : Part 2 : 1987	*Metric units*
BS 699 : 1984	*Specification for copper direct cylinders for domestic purposes*
BS 853	*Specification for vessels for use in heating systems*
BS 853 : Part 1 : 1996	*Calorifiers and storage vessels for central heating and hot water supply*
BS 864	*Capillary and compression tube fittings of copper and copper alloy*
BS 864 : Part 2 : 1983	*Specification for capillary and compression fittings for copper tubes*
BS 1010	*Specification for draw-off taps and stopvalves for water services (screw-down pattern)*
BS 1010 : Part 2 : 1973	*Draw-off taps and above-ground stopvalves*
BS 1212	*Float-operated valves*
BS 1212 : Part 2 : 1990	*Specification for diaphragm type float operated valves (copper alloy body) (excluding floats)*
BS 1212 : Part 3 : 1990	*Specification for diaphragm type float operated valves (plastics bodied) for cold water services only (excluding floats)*
BS 1252 : 1991	*Specification for domestic solid mineral fuel-fired, free-standing cookers with or without boilers*
BS 1394 :	*Stationary circulation pumps for heating and hot water service systems*
BS 1394 : Part 2 : 1987	*Specification for physical and performance requirements*
BS 1566 :	*Copper indirect cylinders for domestic purposes*
BS 1566 : Part 1 : 1984	*Specification for double feed indirect cylinders*
BS 1566 : Part 2 : 1984	*Specification for single feed indirect cylinders*
BS 1710 : 1984	*Specification for identification of pipelines and services*
BS 1894 : 1992	*Specification for design and manufacture of electric boilers of welded construction*
BS 1968 : 1953	*Specification for floats for ballvalves (copper)*
BS 2456 : 1990	*Specification for floats (plastics) for float operated valves for cold water services*
BS 2494 : 1990	*Specification for elastomeric seals for joints in pipework and pipelines*
BS 2580 : 1979	*Specification for underground plug cocks for cold water services*
BS 2871 :	*Specification for copper and copper alloys — Tubes*
BS 2871 : Part 1 : 1971	*Copper tubes for water, gas and sanitation*
BS 2879 : 1980	*Specification for draining taps (screw-down pattern)*
BS 3198 : 1981	*Specification for copper hot water storage combination units for domestic purposes*
BS 3377 : 1985	*Specification for boilers for use with domestic solid mineral fuel appliances*
BS 3378 : 1986	*Specification for room heaters burning solid mineral fuels*
BS 3456 :	*Specification for safety of household and similar electrical appliances*
BS 3456 : Part 2 :	*Particular requirements*
BS 3456 : Section 2.21 : 1972	*Electric immersion heaters*
BS 3456 : Part 102 :	*Particular requirements*
BS 3456 : Section 102.21 : 1988	*Storage water heaters*

BS 3955 : 1986	*Specification for electrical controls for household and similar general purposes*
BS 4127 : 1994	*Specification for light gauge stainless steel tubes, primarily for water applications*
BS 4213 : 1991	*Specification for cold water storage and combined feed and expansion cisterns (polyolefin or olefin copolymer) up to 500 L capacity used for domestic purposes*
BS 4433 :	*Domestic solid mineral fuel fired boilers with rated output up to 45 kW*
BS 4433 : Part 1 : 1994	*Specification for boilers with undergrate ash removal*
BS 4433 : Part 2 : 1994	*Specification for gravity feed boilers designed to burn small anthracite*
BS 4814 : 1990	*Specification for expansion vessels using an internal diaphragm, for sealed hot water heating systems*
BS 4834 : 1990	*Specification for inset open fires without convection with or without boilers, burning solid mineral fuels*
BS 4876 : 1984	*Specification for performance requirements for domestic flued oil burning appliances (including test procedures)*
BS 5163 : 1986	*Specification for predominantly key-operated cast iron gate valves for waterworks purposes*
BS 5258 :	*Safety of domestic gas appliances*
BS 5258 : Part 1 : 1986	*Specification for central heating boilers and circulators*
BS 5258 : Part 8 : 1980	*Combined appliances: gas fire/back boiler*
BS 5258 : Part 15 : 1990	*Specification for combination boilers*
BS 5386 :	*Specification for gas burning appliances*
BS 5386 : Part 1 : 1976	*Gas burning appliances for instantaneous production of hot water for domestic use*
BS 5386 : Part 2 : 1981	*Mini water heaters (2nd and 3rd family gases)*
BS 5386 : Part 5 : 1988	*Specification for gas burning instantaneous water heaters with automatic output variation (2nd and 3rd family gases)*
BS 5422 : 1990	*Method for specifying thermal insulating materials on pipes, ductwork and equipment (in the temperature range −40 °C to + 700 °C)*
BS 5433 : 1976	*Specification for underground stopvalves for water services*
BS 5615 : 1985	*Specification for insulating jackets for domestic hot water storage cylinders*
BS 5728 :	*Measurement of flow of cold potable water in closed conduits*
BS 5728 : Part 1 : 1979	*Specification for single meters*
BS 5871 :	*Specification for installation of gas fires, convector heaters, fire/back boilers and decorative fuel effect gas appliances*
BS 5871 : Part 1 : 1991	*Gas fires, convector heaters and fire/back boilers (1st and 2nd and 3rd family gases)*
BS 5918 : 1989	*Code of practice for solar heating systems for domestic hot water*
BS 6144 : 1990	*Specification for expansion vessels using an internal diaphragm, for unvented hot water supply systems*
BS 6280 : 1982	*Method of vacuum (backsiphonage) test for water-using appliances*
BS 6281 :	*Devices without moving parts for the prevention of contamination of water by backflow*
BS 6281 : Part 1 : 1992	*Specification for type A air gaps*
BS 6281 : Part 2 : 1982	*Specification for type B air gaps*
BS 6281 : Part 3 : 1982	*Specification for pipe interrupters of nominal size up to and including DN 42*

© BSI 1997

BS 6282 :	*Devices with moving parts for the prevention of contamination of water by backflow*
BS 6282 : Part 1 : 1982	*Specification for check valves of nominal size up to and including DN 54*
BS 6282 : Part 2 : 1982	*Specification for terminal anti-vacuum valves of nominal size up to and including DN 54*
BS 6282 : Part 3 : 1982	*Specification for in-line anti-vacuum valves of nominal size up to and including DN 42*
BS 6282 : Part 4 : 1982	*Specification for combined check and anti-vacuum valves of nominal size up to and including DN 42*
BS 6283 :	*Safety and control devices for use in hot water systems*
BS 6283 : Part 1 : 1991	*Specification for expansion valves for pressures up to and including 10 bar*
BS 6283 : Part 2 : 1991	*Specifications for temperature relief valves for pressures from 1 bar to 10 bar*
BS 6283 : Part 3 : 1991	*Specification for combined temperature and pressure relief valves for pressures from 1 bar to 10 bar*
BS 6283 : Part 4 : 1991	*Specification for drop-tight pressure reducing valves of nominal size up to and including DN 50 for supply pressures up to and including 12 bar*
BS 6351 :	*Electric surface heating*
BS 6351 : Part 1 : 1983	*Specification for electric surface heating devices*
BS 6730 : 1986	*Specification for black polyethylene pipes up to nominal size 63 for above ground use for cold potable water*
BS 6798 : 1987	*Specification for installation of gas-fired hot water boilers of rated input not exceeding 60 kW*
BS 6920 :	*Suitability of non-metallic products for use in contact with water for human consumption with regard to their effect on the quality of the water*
BS 6920 : Part 1 : 1990	*Specification*
BS 6920 : Part 2	*Methods of test*
BS 6920 : Part 3 : 1990	*High temperature tests*
BS 6956 :	*Jointing materials and compounds*
BS 6956 : Part 5 : 1992	*Specification for jointing compounds for use with water, low pressure saturated steam, 1st family gases (excluding coal gas) and 2nd family gases*
BS 7206 : 1990	*Specification for unvented hot water storage units and packages*
BS 7430 : 1991	*Code of practice for earthing*
BS 7671 : 1992	*Requirements for electrical installations — IEE Wiring Regulations — Sixteenth edition*
BS 7766 : 1994	*Specification for assessment of the potential for metallic materials to affect adversely the quality of water intended for human consumption*

BS EN 257 : 1992	*Mechanical thermostats for gas-burning appliances*
BS EN 297 : 1994	*Gas-fired central heating boilers — Type B_{11} and B_{11BS} boilers fitted with atmospheric burners of nominal heat input not exceeding 70 kW*
BS EN 545 : 1995	*Ductile iron pipes, fittings, accessories and their joints for water pipelines — Requirements and test methods*
BS EN 598 : 1995	*Ductile iron pipes, fittings, accessories and their joints for sewerage applications — Requirements and test methods*
BS EN 625 : 1996	*Gas fired central heating boilers — Specific requirements for the domestic hot water operation of combination boilers of nominal heat input not exceeding 70 kW.*
BS EN 969 : 1996	*Specification for ductile iron pipes, fittings, accessories and their joints for gas pipelines — Requirements and test methods*
BS EN 60335 :	*Specification for safety of household and similar electrical appliances*
BS EN 60335-2	*Particular requirements*
BS EN 60335-2-21 : 1992	*Storage water heaters*
BS EN 60335-2-35 : 1995	*Instantaneous water heaters*

Other publications

Informative references

BSI publications

BRITISH STANDARDS INSTITUTION, London

BS 534 : 1990	*Specification for steel pipes, joints and specials for water and sewage*
BS 1387 : 1985	*Specification for screwed and socketed steel tubes and tubulars and for plain end steel tubes suitable for welding or for screwing to BS 21 pipe threads*
BS 2872 : 1989	*Specification for copper and copper alloy forging stock and forgings*
BS 2874 : 1986	*Specification for copper and copper alloy rods and sections (other than forging stock)*
BS 3505 : 1986	*Specification for unplasticized polyvinyl chloride (PVC-U) pressure pipes for cold potable water*
BS 4346 :	*Joints and fittings for use with unplasticized PVC pressure pipes*
BS 4346 : Part 1 : 1969	*Injection moulded unplasticized PVC fittings for solvent welding for use with pressure pipes, including potable water supply*
BS 4346 : Part 2 : 1970	*Mechanical joints and fittings, principally of unplasticized PVC*
BS 4346 : Part 3 : 1982	*Specification for solvent cement*
BS 4991 : 1974	*Specification for propylene copolymer pressure pipe*
BS 5114 : 1975	*Specification for performance requirements for joints and compression fittings for use with polyethylene pipes*
BS 5154 : 1991	*Specification for copper alloy globe, globe stop and check, check and gate valves*
BS 5412 : 1996	*Specification for low resistance single taps and combination tap assemblies (nominal size ½ and ¾ suitable for operation at PN 10 max. and a minimum flow pressure of 0.01 MPa (0.1 bar)*
BS 5449 : 1990	*Specification for forced circulation hot water central heating systems for domestic premises*

BS 5493 : 1977	*Code of practice for protective coating of iron and steel structures against corrosion*
BS 5546 : 1990	*Specification for installation of gas hot water supplies for domestic purposes (1st, 2nd and 3rd family gases)*
BS 5834 :	*Surface boxes, guards and underground chambers for gas and waterworks purposes*
BS 5834 : Part 2 : 1983	*Specification for small surface boxes*
BS 6340	*Shower units*
BS 6340 : Part 4 : 1984	*Specification for shower heads and related equipment*
BS 6437 : 1984	*Specification for polyethylene pipes (type 50) in metric diameters for general purposes*
BS 6465 :	*Sanitary installations*
BS 6465 : Part 1 : 1994	*Code of practice for scale of provision, selection and installation of sanitary appliances*
BS 6572 : 1985	*Specification for blue polyethylene pipes up to nominal size 63 for below ground use for potable water*
BS 7291	*Thermoplastics pipes and associated fittings for hot and cold water for domestic purposes and heating installations in buildings*
BS 7291 : Part 1 : 1990	*General requirements*
BS 7291 : Part 2 : 1990	*Specification for polybutylene (PB) pipes and associated fittings*
BS 7291 : Part 3 : 1990	*Specification for crosslinked polyethylene (PE-X) pipes and associated fittings*
BS 7291 : Part 4 : 1990	*Specification for chlorinated polyvinyl chloride (PVC-C) pipes and associated fittings and solvent cement*
CP 312	*Code of practice for plastics pipework (thermoplastics material)*
CP 312 : Part 1 : 1973	*General principles and choice of material*
CP 312 : Part 2 : 1973	*Unplasticized PVC pipework for the conveyance of liquids under pressure*
CP 312 : Part 3 : 1973	*Polyethylene pipes for the conveyance of liquids under pressure*
CP 342	*Code of practice for centralized hot water supply*
CP 342 : Part 2 : 1974	*Buildings other than individual dwellings*
BS EN 200 : 1992	*Sanitary tapware — General technical specifications for single taps and mixer taps (nominal size ½ PN 10 — Minimum flow pressure of 0.05 MPa (0.5 bar))*

© BSI 1997

Other publications

[1] THE WATER RESEARCH CENTRE. *Water fittings and materials directory*, 1995, ISBN 0 1872699–49–9.
[2] CHARTERED INSTITUTION OF BUILDING SERVICES ENGINEERS. *Memorandum* 13, *Minimising the risk of Legionnaires' Disease*, 1987, ISBN 0900953–52–7.
[3] HEALTH AND SAFETY COMMISSION. *Approved Code of Practice. The prevention and control of legionellosis (including Legionnaires' disease)*, ISBN 0 11 885 659– 6, 1995.
[4] HEALTH AND SAFETY EXECUTIVE. *The control of legionellosis including Legionnaires' Disease, Second edition*, 1993, (*HSG* 70), ISBN 0–11–07104519.
[5] THE INSTITUTE OF PLUMBING. *Legionnaires' Disease. Good Practice Guide for Plumbers*, 1990, ISBN 0 9501671 9 3.
[6] NATIONAL HEALTH SERVICE ESTATES. HTM 2040 – *Control of legionellae in health care premises, a code of practice. Consolidated edition* 1991, ISBN 0 11 321334 4.
[7] THE NATIONAL JOINT UTILITIES GROUP. *Publication No.* 6.
[8] HEALTH AND SAFETY EXECUTIVE. *'Safe' hot water and surface temperatures, HS(G)*104, ISBN 0–11–321404–9, 1992.
[9] THE INSTITUTE OF PLUMBING. *Plumbing Engineering Services Design Guide*

© BSI 1997